# MIND, PERCEPTION AND SCIENCE

# MIND, PERCEPTION
# AND SCIENCE

BY

W. RUSSELL BRAIN

D.M., F.R.C.P.

*President of the Royal College of Physicians of London*

BLACKWELL
SCIENTIFIC PUBLICATIONS
OXFORD

First printed, November, 1951

Printed in Great Britain for BLACKWELL SCIENTIFIC PUBLICATIONS LTD
by A. R. MOWBRAY & CO. LIMITED in the City of Oxford

# CONTENTS

The severe schools shall never laugh me out of the philosophy of Hermes, that this visible world is but a picture of the invisible, wherein, as in a portrait, things are not truly, but in equivocal shapes, and as they counterfeit some real substance in that invisible fabrick.

Sir Thomas Browne, *Religio Medici.*

# MIND, PERCEPTION
# AND SCIENCE

## INTRODUCTION

THE advances of science in many spheres have created great
gulfs between the philosophers and the scientific experts,
who possess technical knowledge which the philosophers
lack. This is particularly evident in the realm of the body-
mind relationship, where the philosophers, unfamiliar with
the facts which daily confront the neurologist and the
psychiatrist, either say that there is no problem or that it is
only a pseudo-problem created by the misuse of words.
For many years I have been interested in the disorders of
perception produced by disease of the nervous system.
These show that even the normal process of perception is
far more complex than can be imagined by those whose
acquaintance with the subject is limited to its everyday
vocabulary. Finding that the philosophers provided no
answer to most of my questions I have been compelled to
try to answer them myself, well aware of the pitfalls that
lie in wait for the amateur, but encouraging myself with
the thought that the professionals can hardly disagree with
me more than they do amongst themselves.

Most of this book consists of lectures and broadcasts
delivered during the last five years: and I am grateful to the
editors of the journals in which they were published for
permission to include them. I have revised them and where
necessary translated the neurological terms into less technical

language, which, I hope, will not be beyond the understanding of the general reader. The different occasions account for the differences in style, which I have not attempted to eliminate. I have added a final chapter in which, in the form of a dialogue, I have discussed some of the criticisms of the views I am defending. I have had to omit the discussion of their historical background and of many of their implications. Thus, I have said little about primary and secondary qualities, and nothing about the status of objects. The book falls into two parts. The first three chapters are concerned with neurological questions, and the last four with their philosophical implications. Since the last four chapters are to a large extent self-contained, the general reader with no knowledge of the nervous system may prefer to begin at Chapter IV and read these first.

For at least a century the prevailing philosophical attitude has been determined by the belief, variously expressed, that the 'laws' of matter are fundamental, and that mind is at least potentially capable of explanation in terms of those laws. This idea has had profound effects in all spheres of thought. I believe it to be the product of a mistaken view as to the nature of our knowledge of the mind and the brain respectively, and the relationship between them; and that it is possible to accept all the new knowledge which neurophysiology and psychology can provide, and yet preserve the mind's autonomy in its own sphere. That, at any rate, is the thesis of this book.

# THE NEUROLOGICAL APPROACH TO THE PROBLEM OF PERCEPTION[1]

IT is one of the problems of modern culture that, as the field of knowledge expands and the study of each small portion of it grows more intensive and detailed, it becomes impossible for one man not only to cover the whole field but even to understand the essentials of any but a very small area. A complete discussion of perception, for example, must deal with physics, including atomic physics, the psycho-physiology of the senses, comprising not only normal psychology and physiology, but also clinical neurology, and, finally, philosophy. Here are four highly specialized fields of knowledge. It may be possible for a man to have expert knowledge of two, though even this is exceptional; most of us must be satisfied if we can with difficulty keep abreast with one. So science flourishes, but no one is capable of creating a synthesis or discovering relationships between the facts discovered by the various specialists: indeed, the very facts themselves are often unknown to the philosophers. What then is to be done? Can the specialist become his own philosopher. He is often, I fear, an unsatisfactory one, and his philosophical discoveries are apt to turn out to be respectable but time-worn doctrines. Nevertheless, the scientific specialist-turned-philosopher can at least act as a liaison officer between his specialty and philosophy. He can bring to the notice of the philosopher facts which seem

[1] The Manson Lecture delivered at the British Institute of Philosophy, University Hall, Gordon Square, London, W.C.1, December 14, 1945, reprinted from *Philosophy*, 1946, **21**, 133.

to him significant, and say to him: 'I may well be wrong in my interpretation of these—let me hear what you think.' It is in that spirit that I venture to talk about the neurological approach to the problem of perception. Epistemology seems to me to be the cardinal problem of modern thought, for we cannot separate our conclusions concerning the nature of perceiving from our conclusions as to the nature of what we perceive. As a neurologist I shall be chiefly concerned with the causal aspect of perception. I make no apology for that, for it is much neglected by philosophers, who mostly concentrate upon perception as presentational immediacy. No theory of perception can be adequate which does not fully account for both.

## PHYSIOLOGICAL IDEALISM

In so far as neurologists base any theory of knowledge upon their observations, they seem usually to adopt physiological idealism. The neurologist observes the brains of animals and of other people. From the behaviour of both, and from the answers which patients give to his questions, he discovers that, when an object is perceived, a series of events occurs successively in time, beginning with an event in the object and ending with an event in the subject's brain. If the series is interrupted at any point between the object and the cerebral cortex (brain surface) of the subject, the object is not perceived. If the relevant area of the cortex is destroyed, the object again is not perceived. But if the relevant area of the cortex is electrically stimulated while the subject is conscious, sense-data of a kind aroused by an object are perceived by the subject. Thus it is held that the event immediately preceding, or perhaps synchronous with, the perception of the object is an event of a physico-chemical kind in the subject's cerebral cortex. The cortical neurones are normally excited in the way just described from the external world, but if they should exceptionally be excited in some other way—for example, by electrical stimulation or by an epileptic discharge—the appropriate sense-data would still be experienced. The only independently necessary condition for the awareness of sense-data, to use Broad's term,[1] is thus an event in the cerebral cortex. This might be true and yet the awareness of sense-data might still be compatible with the possession by sense-data of some status in the world external to the subject's brain. But the neurologist goes on to argue that this cannot be so for reasons which are important enough to deserve detailed consideration, whether or not his conclusion from them is right.

Let us examine the account which the neurophysiologist gives of the causation of sense-data. I shall take my first illustration from hearing, because the physics of sound is easier to understand than that of light. A tuning-fork is struck or a whistle is blown, or in some other way the air is made to vibrate, and a series of waves with a frequency of, let us say, 4,000 vibrations a second is propagated through the air. It strikes the observer's ear and a portion of the cochlea, attuned to this particular frequency, is caused to vibrate at the same rate. So far the subject has heard nothing. The vibration of this part of the cochlea starts a series of nerve-impulses in a certain fibre or fibres of the auditory nerve. No nerve-fibre in the body can carry impulses at so fast a rate. The frequency with which nerve-impulses can follow one another along a nerve depends upon the electro-chemical structure of nervous tissue and is never more than 1,500 a second, and often much less. We learn this by recording electrically the response of nerves to their appropriate stimuli. The auditory nerve-fibre therefore conducts

[1] *Scientific Thought*, London, 1927, 501.

impulses at its accustomed rate, and, by a series of relay paths, the impulses reach the auditory area of the cerebral cortex in the temporal lobe. Electro-encephalography enables us to detect its arrival there and in the experimental animal we can record simultaneously the frequency of the sound-stimulus, and the electrical response which it evokes in the auditory cortex. These are entirely dissimilar. Frequencies of stimulus ranging from 100 to 16,000 vibrations a second evoke the same kind of electrical response from the auditory cortex; namely, a single deflection lasting from 1/20 to 1/55 second. But the auditory stimuli of different frequencies excite different nerve fibres conveying impulses to different areas of the cortex. In the dog the cortical foci responsive to high frequencies are located in front and those for low frequencies behind, and successive octaves are arranged at equal intervals along the cortex (Tunturi).[1] Similar observations have been made on the cat (Woolsey and Walzl),[2] and since they depend upon certain properties of nervous tissue and structure, there is no reason to think that man is essentially different. Now the difference in pitch of two sounds is correlated with a difference in their frequencies, but no such difference is to be found in the events in the nervous system upon which the discrimination of their respective sense-data depends. These have neither the frequencies of the simuli nor do they differ from each other in frequency. They differ only in that the nervous impulses travel by different paths and reach different destinations in the cerebral cortex; and this seems to be true not only of the difference between one sound and another, but also of that between the nervous impulses evoked by auditory, visual and olfactory stimuli. As Adrian[3] says: 'The quality of the sensation seems to depend on the path

---

[1] *Amer. J. Physiol.*, 1944, **141**, 397.    [2] *Amer. J. Physiol.*, 1941, **133**, 498.
[3] *The Basis of Sensation*, London, 1938.

which the impulses must travel, for apart from this there is little to distinguish the messages from different receptors.'

Thus, according to neurophysiology, the observer is like a deaf housemaid who sits in her kitchen and watches the indicators of the electric bells. There are different bell-pushes (receptors) outside the front door and the back door and in the various rooms, but similar currents travel along similar wires, and the only difference she can detect is that different indicators move. Being paralysed as well as deaf she never answers the bell except by pressing another one!

The facts of neurophysiology are held to mean that sense-data are 'really' located either in the cerebral cortex or in the mind of the observer. It is then necessary to inquire why a coloured patch which is 'really' in my brain or in my mind appears to be outside me on a table in the room. The physiological idealist replies by invoking a process which he calls 'projection.' The colour is 'really' in my brain, but I 'project' it in some way on to the table.

For various reasons it is difficult to believe that such a process occurs. Some of the objections have often been pointed out. The physiological idealist, it has been well said, is an idealist in respect of other people's sense-data and a realist in respect of his own. For, if all sense-data are states of his brain, this must also be true of the sense-data derived from his own body; and his brain itself, if, as is not impossible, he could see it in a mirror in the course of an operation, must be reduced to an activity of itself. No doubt he will try and save the situation by maintaining that his sense-data give him information concerning objects which exist independently of his awareness of them. But it is difficult to see how he could ever arrive at this conclusion if his sense-data were nothing but states of his own brain. How does the deaf and paralysed housemaid, who was born in the kitchen and has never been outside it, know that the electric bell indicators give her information as to what is happening at the front door or the back door? How does she know that anything exists outside the kitchen? These are well-known philosophical objections to physiological idealism. There is one difficulty, however, which neurophysiology itself raises.

Let us suppose that we are watching an observer looking at a circle. There is a sense-datum or a group of sense-data which are circular. Light waves, which in their grouping maintain a circular relationship, travel from the object to the eyes of the observer. On a circular area on each of his two retinae disturbances are set up which excite nervous impulses which travel through his optic nerves, tracts and radiations to the visual areas of the cerebral cortex. Only when the nervous impulses reach the cortex does the observer see the circle. If physiological idealism is true we might expect to find that there is something circular about the events at the cerebral cortex, for it is these, we are told, which are 'projected' on to the outside world when we perceive a circle. Nothing of the sort is true. The area of cortical excitation which exists when we perceive a circle is divided into two halves, one in each cerebral hemisphere. Pathways connecting them exist, but these appear to play no part in our perception of the two halves of a circle as one whole, for this still occurs when the connecting pathway (the corpus callosum) is divided.[1] Neither half is semicircular; it is roughly the shape of ▬, the closed end lying in front and the open end behind. The right half of the circle is represented in the left cerebral hemisphere and vice versa, and the lower quadrant is represented above the upper. There is another complication. We saw that a circular nervous disturbance occurred in each retina; thus each half of the circle has a double representation in the

---

[1] Akelaitis, A. J., *Arch. Neurol. Psychiat.*, 1941, **45**, 288.

nervous system, and, though the pathways for the two corresponding halves—that is, the two right halves and the two left halves—come to be close together behind the optic chiasma, and are represented in the same area of the cerebral cortex, there is no anatomical point at which they fuse, as Sherrington[1] demonstrated in his experiments with flicker. Finally, since the two halves of the circle are represented in cortical areas lying parallel to each other, the cortical disturbance is three-dimensional.

Thus when we perceive a two-dimensional circle we do so by means of an activity in the brain which is halved, re-duplicated, transposed, inverted, distorted, and three-dimensional. If physiological idealism is to be really physiological it must admit that its theory of projection breaks down because the circle which is said to be projected from the cerebral cortex never existed there at all.

## REALISM

Now let us turn to a consideration of some alternative theories—those which have in common the belief that sense-data in some way exist independently of our aware-ness of them, and compose or help to compose objects, and that thus our perception of objects involves and depends upon our discovery or selection of sense-data and not our creation of them. This view seems to me to encounter difficulties as formidable as those which confront physiological idealism. Let us consider some of them.

However little interest realist philosophers may take in the causal aspects of perception, they all seem to accept the view that it must be, at any rate theoretically, possible to give a causal account of perception which shall relate events occurring in the object to events in the brain of the

---

[1] *The Integrative Action of the Nervous System*, London, 1906, 354 *et seq.*

observer and finally to events in his consciousness. Thus when I perceive a brown patch there are wave-lengths of a given frequency, nervous impulses and so on, even though it may be difficult or impossible to say how this series of events is related to awareness of a brown sense-datum Now between one colour and another, between brown and green, black and white, there are differences of quality by which we distinguish them; there is also something in common, colouredness, which enables us to group them together. But suppose instead of a brown patch we consider a black patch. What are the wave-length and frequency of black light? Of course there are none. Black is a sense-datum of the same kind as brown, or even white: in fact, they shade into one another so that it may be impossible to say where one ends and the other begins—but no causal account can be given of our perception of black in terms of excitations proceeding from the object. Indeed, the perception of black depends upon the absence of such visual excitations. It also depends upon the integrity of the visual part of the cerebral cortex. Seeing black is not the same as not seeing white or any other colour. If one-half of the visual cortex is destroyed so that the subject fails to see half of his visual field it does not appear black to him. He merely fails to see it, and may even be unaware that it is lost. I hope a realist philosopher will give us an account of the ontological status of a black sense-datum when it is not being perceived, and, in particular, its relationship to its non-existent substratum in the physical world. I suspect that it will prove to belong to the family of sense-data comprising that famous non-existent black cat in the dark room. And if a black sense-satum is to be regarded as in some way generated or created by the brain or the mind, what reason have we for thinking that this is not equally true of a brown or blue sense-datum, for it would seem that external excitation does not necessarily determine the quality of a sense-datum. Indeed, our experience of dreams should have taught us that, for we experience visual sense-data when asleep in a dark room.

This brings me to another class of sense-data which need have no external excitation; namely, hallucinations. Realist philosophers treat these as 'wild' sense-data. Price,[1] referring to pink rats, says: 'Three things are indubitably real: the sensing, the sense-datum, and the act of perceptual consciousness. Only one thing is not real—the material thing which is the object of his perceptual consciousness.' But the only conditions either dependently or independently necessary for the perception of hallucinations are states of the subject's body. I cannot discover any evidence for the view that the pink rats exist unperceived as wild sense-data, and that perceiving them is a process of catching them in the trap of consciousness. It is a relief to know that Price thinks that the wild sense-data may be 'fleeting entities,' but, if so, how do they come into existence apart from the process which leads to their being perceived?

Let us turn now to another kind of hallucination—the phantom limb. It is well known that a person who has lost a limb may continue to experience the feeling that it is there, and this is called a 'phantom limb.' It is, perhaps, less well known that it is not necessary for the limb to be amputated in order that a phantom limb may be experienced. Interruption of the sensory pathways at various levels of the nervous system may have the same result. Then the patient may see his limb in one position and feel as if he has another in another position. Let us consider the simpler case of the amputated limb. The limb is felt to be where in fact it is not: it may even be felt to be in a part of space occupied by another solid object. 'Wild' sense-data,

[1] *Perception*, London, 1932, 147.

B

in the realist view, do in fact exist at that spot, but these cannot be caused by events occurring where they are experienced in the phantom limb: they must be generated in some other part of the body. They possess, however, qualitative and spatial characteristics indistinguishable from those which are caused by events occurring where they are experienced. What reason, then, have we for thinking that the qualitative and spatial characteristics of sense-data related to a limb which is really there are not similarly generated elsewhere; for example, in the brain or the mind of the observer?

## THE ROLE OF THE BODY IN PERCEPTION

The part played by the body in our perception of the external world is of the greatest importance, and is much neglected by realist philosophers. Whitehead[1] alone among recent philosophers seems to me to give due weight to it. Let us begin by considering a relatively simple experience. I am holding a stone in my hand and I perceive that it feels smooth, hard, cold and of a certain shape. Realism maintains that in doing so I am aware of sense-data simultaneously and successively, and that these sense-data belong to the object and exist either as actual or obtainable sense-data independently of my perceiving them. Now Price[2] has observed what he calls 'a curious point' about touch. 'All normal tactual sense-data,' he says, 'belong to two objects at once; namely, to the object which we are touching, and to our own body or some part of it.' I should prefer to say that tactile sense-data may belong to either. Suppose that I stroke someone's skin with a fine wisp of cotton-wool, and ask what he feels. He may

---

[1] See *Process and Reality*, Cambridge, 1939, 89, 104–5, 167–8, 178.
[2] Loc. cit., 229.

reply 'a tickling sensation' or 'a piece of wool.' In the first case he is describing a sense-datum in his skin, in the second he is referring it to an object. But it may be said in the second case he is merely inferring that the sense-datum in his skin has been caused by an object with which previous experience has made him familiar. But take another example. When my hand has been exposed to cold air, I say, 'My hand is cold,' but when I grasp a stone I say, 'This stone is cold.' In each case what I am experiencing is a cold sense-datum, but in the one case I feel it in my hand and in the other case as belonging to an object. How do I perceive the size, shape and solidity of the stone? The touch and pressure sense-data which contact with the object evokes in my fingers are localized and distinguished as relating to different parts of the skin. Furthermore, my fingers themselves will be bent or straightened and separated to a greater or less extent; and each successive movement and posture of any finger arouses sense-data from the tendons and joints. If you move your fingers when your eyes are closed you are aware of these sense-data as originating in and referring to your fingers; but if you are holding an object in your hand these sense-data become fused with those just described and are felt as collectively conveying awareness of the size, shape and solidity of the object. Thus all the sense-data which are said to belong to an object when it is handled can in suitable conditions be experienced as belonging to the body.

But the body is present in our perceptions in a more elusive and less perceptible fashion. The realist usually starts from awareness of sense-data. Thus Price[1] says that when we see a tomato 'something is red and round then and there I cannot doubt.' It is, then, assumed that we can go on to consider this red and round something as an

[1] Loc. cit., 3.

entity independent of its then-and-thereness. Most realist philosophers, I suppose, would maintain that the red patch is or is composed of sense-data, and that its thereness is not. But how do I arrive at the awareness that the red patch is 'there.' Because the images which it throws on my two retinae are slightly different, because the accommodation of my eyes is contracted or relaxed, because the axes of my eyes are at a certain angle and certain ocular muscles are contracted or relaxed. All these states of my body cause nervous impulses to reach my brain. They, however, would tell me little if I did not also receive impulses from my labyrinths, which vary according to the position of my head in space, and from the muscles and joints of my neck, which indicate the position of my head in relation to my body. In other words, the spatial setting of the red patch is derived from my body; and the proof of this is that when this bodily machinery goes wrong I no longer see the red patch 'there.' I see two red patches, or the red patch goes round and round, or though I see it, I simply do not know where it is, and cannot find my way to it. Hence my awareness of the red patch depends to a surprising extent upon nervous impulses from my body, some of which remain unconscious though others give rise to recognizable somatic sense-data. We can consider the red patch as an isolated sense-datum but we cannot experience it so, and, in so far as we consider it so, our consideration is remote from experience. The total experience of 'a red patch there' contains subjective somatic sense-data inextricably intermingled with it.

In an attack of migraine the patient experiences visual hallucinations of scintillating lights seen to one or other side. These are caused by a disturbance at the visual cortex on one side. Let such a patient during the attack lie with closed eyes in a dark room. If now he turns his eyes to the right the hallucinatory figure appears to move to the right and similarly in any other direction. Thus, nervous impulses from the eye muscles evoked by the movement of the eyes determine where a hallucination originating at the visual cortex shall be seen.

There is another example which beautifully illustrates how perception and causal investigation may aid each other. If I am in a completely dark room with my eyes closed I see a black expanse which seems to be very near me if not actually behind my eyelids. If now I open my eyes, the black expanse appears to be outside me at some distance. Where I perceive the black sense-datum therefore depends upon nervous impulses from the muscles which open and close my eyes, since nothing else has changed.

Electro-encephalography shows (Adrian)[1] that, when the eyes are closed, there is a steady electrical rhythm detectable over the visual cortex. This is abolished by opening the eyes and looking at something, but it is also abolished by opening the eyes in a completely dark room. Opening the eyes thus causes an electrical change in the visual cortex contemporary with the spatial change perceived in the black sense-datum, though, be it noted, there is no change in anything outside the body.

There are other objections to realism which seem to me serious, but I will mention only one. Astronomical distances are so great that light takes many years to travel to us from distant stars. The star which I now see may have ceased to exist since it sent out the light rays which are striking my retina. In what sense, other than a causal one, can my sense-datum be said to belong to a non-existent star? This is an extreme but not a special instance, for the same is true of all perception. All physical impulses upon which perception depends take time to reach us from all

[1] *Trans. Ophth. Soc. United Kingdom*, 1943, **63**, 196.

objects. The speed of light is so great relative to terrestrial distances that we can usually neglect it, but the fact remains that I can never see anything but the immediate past of any object I look at.[1] Sound travels slowly in relation to the speed of modern aeroplanes; hence this discrepancy becomes of practical importance. The aeroplane which I hear in one place has now moved to another. I am hearing its past. This is true even of bodily sensation, since a nervous impulse takes a measurable time to travel from the sense organ to the brain. I can feel only the immediate past of any part of my own body except the brain. Sense-data, then, are part of my present, but how can they form part of physical objects of whose present I can know nothing and which may even have ceased to exist?

## Awareness of Externality

Thus I must confess that I find both physiological ideal- ism, as ordinarily stated, and the varieties of critical realism equally unsatisfactory. I must now briefly try to indicate at least the lines along which it seems to me we should seek for a method of reconciling the data of presentational immediacy with the data which science provides concerning perception in its causal aspects.

Externality is the cardinal problem. X sees a tomato on the table. Something happens in X's brain and he sees a red patch outside him. How are these two statements related? I say 'two statements' and not 'two events' because I do not think there are two events. At the reflex level, organisms show adaptations to space without awareness of it. Many reflexes have a spatial character. If a harmful stimulus is applied to the hind foot of the spinal frog,

[1] Relativity theory defines as contemporaneous those events which cannot be causally related to each other. Conversely, causally related events cannot be contemporaneous.

though it cannot be felt, the foot is reflexly withdrawn out of harm's way. The righting reflexes orientate the organism in relation to gravity. Involuntary blinking in response to an object approaching the eye is a reflex which is evoked by spatial changes outside the body. All the proprioceptive and postural reflexes are responses to spatial factors and modify the position of the body or its segments in space.

In our awareness of our own bodies we are directly aware of a three-dimensional object.[1] The position of this object can be changed in relation to the external world and the position of its parts can be modified in relation to the body as a whole. Thus the body serves as a primary model of three-dimensional space.

The body surface provides examples of externality. To discriminate between different parts of the surface of the body is to recognize that they possess the relationship of mutual externality. If I clasp one hand with the other I am aware of each hand as external to the other. I am both subject and object, and I am directly aware of the spatial position of both.

The discrimination of different parts of the body's surface depends upon the fact that each is separately represented on the surface of the brain. Thus the same relationship of externality exists between the two areas of the body surface and the two areas of brain surface. The same is true of two areas of the retina and two areas of the visual cortex.

[1] Awareness of the body has been held to give rise to a body schema or image. However convenient in practice, these terms are easily interpreted as implying a dualism which I think is epistemologically objectionable. The most important literature on awareness of the body consists of a paper by Head, H., and Holmes, G., Studies in Neurology, London, 1920, 2, 605; The Image and Appearance of the Human Body, by Paul Schilder, London, 1935; the same author's Mind, Perception and Thought in their Constructive Aspects, New York, 1942; L'Image de Notre Corps, by Jean Lhermite, Paris, 1939, and some recent work is discussed in my paper in Brain, 1941, 64, 244.

Now suppose that instead of clasping one hand with the other I am looking at my hand. An image is formed on my retinae and an area in my visual cortex is excited. I move my fingers. There is a simultaneous change in two cortical areas—the visual cortex and an area in which are represented the surface and posture of my hand as felt. Both movements are related to my body image as a whole. I knew where my fingers were to start with, and I know where they are now that I have moved them. The awareness which is the conscious representation of what is happening at my visual cortex, in other words, the visual image of my hand, is located at that point in my body image where my hand is felt to be.

Now let us suppose that I hold a tomato in my hand. In addition to the position of my hand in my body image I am now conscious of tactile and postural sense-data, described above, as evoked by the tomato in my hand, and in addition to the visual image of my hand there are now the visual sense-data associated with the tomato. Both tactually and visually the tomato is in my hand, the position of which is already related to my body image. And if I now put the tomato on the table, I bring my hand into a new position on the table and leave the tomato there; and its visual sense-data now occupy a position which is related to my body by being known as having just been occupied by my hand. Without attempting to define how much of space-perception we owe to innate dispositions and how much to experience we can say that this is the essence of the genesis of awareness of externality, first through the sense of touch and then through vision; and one has only to watch a baby a few months old exploring its own body and manipulating and dropping objects to see the process at work. Though, so far as I know, no philosopher has ever mentioned it, 'dropableness' is the primary quality which distinguishes a small object from a part of one's body.

But this simple outline requires to be filled in with some details. When I bend my head to look at my hand I excite my vestibular apparatus and the nerves of my neck; I converge and accommodate my eyes; and nervous impulses, conscious or unconscious, pour in to contribute to the modifications of my body image.

Time plays an important part in our awareness of space. When I bend my elbow I am aware not only of the movement but of the time taken to effect it. This factor becomes much more important when the whole body moves. Then time is implicit in space, for time is taken to traverse a distance; and the changing bodily and environmental sense-data experienced in the course of the journey are felt to be successive. Thus there is a sense in which even in perception what we are aware of is space-time, from which space is an abstraction.

Spatial relations as primarily perceived are thus somatocentric. The final task of space-perception is the recognition of an absolute three-dimensional space by the creation of invariants, as Pötzl[1] puts it, so that the identity of visual objects is maintained independently of the relation-system in which they are at the moment arranged.

## THE NEUROLOGICAL DISTINCTION BETWEEN PRIMARY AND SECONDARY QUALITIES

Thus when we study perception in its causal mode we find that the nervous system is extremely well adapted for the representation of relationships existing in the physical world, including the mutual externality of objects, among

---

[1] *Die Aphasialehre vom Standpunkte der Klinischen Psychiatrie*, Bd. 1. Die optisch-agnostischen Störungen, Leipzig, 1928.

which is the body. Furthermore, mutual externality and spatial multiplicity are different ways of describing the same relationship. The whole of science is built up upon the exact correspondence between the multiplicity of objects in the physical world and the excitation of multiple areas of the cerebral cortex. But what consciousness is aware of is never simply the anatomical relationships of cortical areas: it is the relationship subsisting in the external world, which is presented to consciousness by the dynamic inter-play of a highly complex integration of impulses from different sense-organs, some excited from without the body and some from within.

But, though the body is well adapted to the task of spatial discrimination, temporal succession sets it a different and much more difficult problem. Nervous tissue possesses peculiar features: in particular, a peripheral nerve cannot conduct continuously but only by means of a succession of impulses, the frequency and rate of conduction of which vary within narrow limits, and differ little from one form of sensation to another. Thus there appears to be nothing in the conduction of nervous impulses to correspond to the great differences between light, sound and touch regarded as physical stimuli, and, as we have seen, this is one of the main arguments of the physiological idealist in favour of the view that sense-data must be quite different from anything in the external world.

Every sensory nerve has its receptor organ, which is stimulated by, and hence attuned to, its particular stimulus. A constant stimulus, suddenly initiated, sets up, as Adrian[1] has shown, a continuous though diminishing excitatory state at the nerve-ending, which excites a series of dis-continuous impulses in the nerve. Finally, there occurs a sense-datum which is continuous but diminishes in intensity.

[1] *The Basis of Sensation*, London, 1928, 119.

In order that a physical stimulus may arouse a sense-datum it must have a certain minimum duration. Neurophysiology, in giving an account of the phenomena of the sensory impulse, describes these in its own way as a succession of spatial states: but this is to neglect the essential feature of living matter. The process of awareness of a sense-datum begins at the receptor organ with a four-dimensional event—the receptor organ experiencing a physical stimulus for a minimum duration. Since there is as yet no awareness, I shall borrow Whitehead's term 'prehension' and say that at the level of the receptor there is a prehension of the successiveness of a physical stimulus into a four-dimensional multiplicity-in-unity. Thence onwards in the nervous system I suggest that we are dealing with the conduction of such prehensions, which no three-dimensional account can adequately describe. When they reach the cerebral cortex, where they are integrated with other impulses, we are aware of sense-data. Thus, broadly speaking, primary qualities correspond to those relations between sense-data which are spatially discriminated by means of the cerebral cortex as an area extended in space, and secondary qualities are those sense-data which are prehended through the capacity of nervous tissue to create a new kind of four-dimensional unity out of successiveness.

To sum up, I find perceptual awareness so impregnated with somatic sense-data, that even the perceptual distinction between my body and external objects does not correspond to a distinction between somatic and non-somatic sense-data. But I believe that many relations which exist between sense-data are identical with those which exist between physical objects, and that secondary qualities are generated by our brains. I cannot discover any meaning in the statement that sense-data, even hallucinatory sense-data, are not where they appear to be. But any description of the relation between sense-data and objects must take account of the fact that perceptual awareness is never contemporaneous with the events it portrays. We are always anything from a fraction of a second to a few thousand years behind the times.

# II

## SPEECH AND THOUGHT[1]

IN this chapter I want to attempt to answer the question—
are there functions of the nervous system which are at the
same time both physiological and psychological? I don't
mean by this occurrences like the electrical changes which
can be detected in the back of the brain when we see, for
since we do not know the connection between the electrical changes and seeing, they take us no further. But, are
there events in the brain which we can understand as being
at the same time both physiological and mental? I believe
that there are, and it is in the realm of speech and thought
that we shall find them, even though at the moment they
are little more than dim outlines seen through the mist of our
ignorance.

As we all know, speech has two sides to it; we listen to
speech and we speak ourselves. I shall not here say anything
about the second aspect of speech, which consists of the
utterance of words: I shall confine myself to what has been
called the receptive side; that is, the understanding of words
which we hear and read. This element in speech seems, in
fact, to be more closely related to thinking than the means
by which we express our thoughts when we have already
arrived at them.

When someone speaks and another person listens it may
seem a very simple process, but, in fact, it is so extremely
complicated that it is very difficult to understand. Let
us take as an example the word 'dog.' No two people

[1] Reprinted from *The Physical Basis of Mind*, edited by Peter Laslett, Basil
Blackwell, Oxford, 1950.

pronounce the word 'dog' in exactly the same way, yet we always know what it means. Not only that, it can be sung, shouted or whispered and it still conveys the same thing. The puzzle arises from the fact that each different way of pronouncing 'dog' causes a different electrical disturbance in the nervous system. High-pitched notes go to one spot on the surface of the brain and low-pitched notes go to another which, though not far away, is quite distinct. So if a voice is high-pitched it will start electrical currents moving in one place in the brain, and if it is low-pitched in another, and every variation in the inflection of a voice will produce a different electrical disturbance in the brain of the hearer. And yet he will always hear and understand the same word.

But we can go further than that. The written word 'dog' will still mean the same thing, though the word no longer consists of sounds, but is made up of black marks on a white piece of paper; it can still be understood, whether it is written or printed, in large or small letters, in black or coloured type, and in any sort of handwriting short of complete illegibility: in many handwritings the marks that people make on the paper have very little resemblance to the letters they are supposed to represent. Here, then, there is as great a variety among the visual patterns presented to the nervous system as among spoken words. Moreover, the patterns of things we see send electrical impulses to a different part of the brain from that which is concerned with hearing. The brain's quite separate centres for the sense of touch can also be brought in. The reader of braille can recognize a series of raised pimples on the paper, which make a pattern quite unlike ordinary letters, and yet also mean the word 'dog.'

In the brain there is a complicated set of nervous pathways, like a whole series of electrical circuits, which are thrown into activity whenever we think of the meaning of the word 'dog'; and there are different sets of nervous pathways for other words. The problem, therefore, is to explain how a single set of pathways, those concerned with the meaning of the word 'dog,' can be selected from all the others and set going by any one of that indefinitely large number of different groups of sounds and patterns on paper which constitute all the possible ways of saying, or writing, or printing the word so that it can be understood. When I dial an automatic telephone exchange I ask it a question to which I hope to receive an accurate answer, namely, the subscriber to whom I wish to speak, but the machine is very particular about the way in which I put the question. If I want Whitehall 1212, I must dial WHI 1212 and nothing else. No machine has been designed which will answer with Whitehall 1212 if I or anyone else *speak* the words and figures into the mouthpiece. Only the human brain can do this. Until the dialling machine was designed to standardize the way the question is asked, the human brain of the telephone operator had to be employed at the exchange. Now I do not think it is theoretically impossible to design a machine which could answer fairly accurately to the spoken voice, but I suspect that if it ever is made it will have to embody the same principles upon which the human brain works.

Perhaps, after all, the automatic telephone does provide a clue to what happens in the brain. What the dialling apparatus does is to convert the letters and figures of the telephone number into a certain pattern of electrical impulses in time and space, which is different for each number. What the brain does with the spoken word—and no one can say how it does it—is to extract from it an electrical pattern in time and space which is distinctive of the word 'dog,' and common to all the ways in which it can be pronounced, so as to be recognized. It is as though the meaning of the word were locked up in a cupboard which had to be opened by a key. The curious thing is that it is possible to open it by a very large number of keys which superficially seem to be very different from one another. But what makes a key open a lock is a certain kind of pattern. The pattern of the key must be appropriate to the pattern of the lock, and, if it is appropriate, it does not matter whether the key is made of brass, or steel, or silver, or even gold. In the brain the patterns are very complicated electrical ones. All the possible ways of pronouncing the word 'dog' so that it can be understood have something in common; that is, a certain pattern of sound. This in turn is capable of exciting in the nervous system its own particular pattern of nervous circuits, and this constitutes the key that unlocks the door which contains the meaning of the word. In somewhat the same way all the different ways of writing or printing the word 'dog' arouse a common pattern in a different part of the brain and this also fits the lock of the meaning.

All this complex process goes on in our brains without our knowing anything about it. We hear or read the word and we know what it means, but we know nothing at first hand about the processes which form the link between the two. Sometimes we lose the key either temporarily or, as a result of disease, permanently. You have forgotten someone's name: let us suppose it is 'Johnson': I ask you if it is Smith, Brown, or Robinson, and you reject all these. 'Is it Johnson?' I say, and you say at once, 'Yes, that is it!' When you did not know what the name was, how did you know it was not Smith, Brown, or Robinson? Because these keys did not fit the lock, and when I offered you Johnson it fitted, and at once you realized that that was the key you had lost. This illustrates the point that there are processes in the recognition of words of which we are not conscious. What I have called the lock must be unconscious, for you used the Johnson lock to test the key, yet your possession of the lock did not by itself enable you to remember the name.

Now let us turn to thought and consider an abstract idea: let us choose the idea of triangularity. A rat can be trained to recognize a triangle and distinguish it from a square or a circle; such a rat may be said to be aware of triangularity. The process in the nervous system by means of which a rat recognizes a triangle is of the same kind as that by which a human being recognizes a word. The pattern of excitement aroused in the rat's nervous system by all sorts of triangles has something in common which is distinct from that aroused by other geometrical figures, and this common pattern influences the rat's behaviour.

It would be possible to teach a child to recognize a triangle in the same way as a rat is taught. A child might be shown a variety of figures and given a chocolate when it chose a triangle and a punishment when it chose anything else. But since we can speak to a child we can take a short cut and say, 'A triangle is a figure bounded by three straight lines.' We shall then have to use words to enable the child to grasp an abstract idea. But we must not forget that someone must have had the idea of a triangle before it could be described in words. So speech and thought interact. If we are to name something, the nervous system must be capable of recognizing a common pattern in a number of different objects; and, when an object has already been named, this in itself helps us to detect what it has in common with other objects of the same name. We can get along very well in simple matters without using words for our thinking, but as soon as we have to think about things which are not concrete objects we find it difficult to think without

C

words. If you go into a room and find the cat on the table drinking the milk, you take in the situation and act appropriately without formulating, even in your own mind, the words 'cat,' 'table' and 'milk,' though you would have to do so if you wanted to draw the attention of someone else to what was happening. But consider this sentence from Plato: 'Can there be any greater evil in the state than discord and distraction and plurality where unity ought to reign?' We cannot think about the ideas contained in that sentence without using words for the purposes of our thought.

I have spoken earlier about the meaning of a word. Without going into the much-debated philosophical question of the meaning of meaning I want to point out that we use the term meaning in at least two different ways. Let us take as an example a proper name—'St. Paul's Cathedral.' In one sense these words mean—that is, they refer to—a certain building in London. But in another sense, when I say that I know what they mean I am saying that they enable me to think of that building, and what I think of it will depend upon my past experience of it. If I have seen it, I shall perhaps form a mental picture of its dome rising above London. If not, I may think of a service broadcast from it, or of Harrison Ainsworth's novel, *Old St. Paul's*, or of the cathedral of which John Donne was dean. Any or all of these are, as we put it, what St. Paul's Cathdral *means* to me. So in this sense the meaning of a word implies its power to awaken in us all kinds of past associations, ideas and feelings, and sometimes memory-images, and these must depend upon numerous and widespread pathways irradiating over the surface and deep into the substance of the brain. Yet clearly we can speak the word and know what it means without calling up any of these associations, so that often in conversation the words

'St. Paul's Cathedral' just stand for all these potential associations without necessarily making us conscious of any of them. We are able to do this because there exists in the brain an electrical pattern for each word which is not identical with those underlying either its sound or its meaning.

Here we have reached the foundation of all language—the fact that a word can stand for the concrete thing or the abstract idea which it represents. But the value—and also the danger—of words for the purposes of thought is that though they are linked with their meanings we can deal with them as though they were relatively independent of them. We treat them as counters, or bank-notes, or cheques, so that, as the philosopher Leibniz put it, we can perform complicated operations with them and wait until these operations are concluded before converting the results into coins. But words would be useless for thinking if they did not retain below the surface of our minds their links with their meanings; and it was the constant task of Socrates, as it is of philosophers to-day, to persuade people to examine the meanings of the words they use.

Now let me try and sum up what I have said. All stimuli, whether sights, sounds or other sensations, reach the brain as electrical patterns, and it seems to be a basic function of the nervous system to analyse these patterns so as to detect similarity amidst differences. A rat can distinguish a triangle from other geometrical figures, and this is the beginning of abstract thought. We do the same thing with words. The word 'dog' for the nervous system is not simply any of the thousand and one ways in which it can be pronounced: it is also an electrical pattern which is called up by each and all of them and of which we are not even conscious. The function of this electrical pattern is to arouse other patterns—those underlying ideas, feelings and perhaps memory-images, which is what the word means to us and through which we know what it refers to. We can think to some extent without words, but only in rather a concrete way: we cannot entertain abstract ideas without using them. But when we think with words we often use them, like counters, to stand for things or ideas, in order to save ourselves the trouble of having to think every time about the things or ideas themselves. To that extent we are all like the little girl who was told to think before she spoke, and replied: 'But how can I know what I think till I hear what I say?'

Is it likely that physiology will ever throw any real light upon the relationship between the brain and the mind? I believe that, working in conjunction with psychology, it will. I can only guess where present advances seem to be leading us. Think of a pattern. An atom is a pattern of electrons, a molecule is a pattern of atoms. There are patterns of patterns of patterns, and so on indefinitely. The most complicated patterns we know are in the brain. Not only are there twelve thousand million nerve cells out of which the patterns can be made, but nervous patterns exist in time, like a melody, as well as in space. If you look at a tapestry through a magnifying glass you will see the individual threads but not the pattern: if you stand away from it you will see the pattern but not the threads. My guess is that in the nervous system we are looking at the threads while with the mind we perceive the patterns, and that one day we may discover how the patterns are made out of the threads.

# III

## THE CEREBRAL BASIS OF
## CONSCIOUSNESS[1]

WHAT do we mean by consciousness? Consciousness is not something which we can define in terms of anything else: we can only indicate its meaning denotatively; that is, by pointing to instances of it. When I hear a sound or see a colour, remember something, experience an emotion or think, I am conscious. Consciousness is a quality which these states, which we call conscious states, have in common, but there is no reason to suppose that it exists independently of them. There is no such thing as consciousness apart from conscious states, any more than there is redness apart from red objects. This may seem obvious, but it leads to the conclusion that we can study consciousness only by studying conscious states, and that we may be able to learn about it from any state in which it is manifested. My object in this chapter is to try in part to answer the question: what is happening in the nervous system when we are experiencing a conscious state? I do not propose to discuss why changes in the nervous system are associated with consciousness.

### LOCAL SIGN IN SENSATION

Let us begin by considering what is involved in the simplest possible experience of a bodily sensation, a touch, let us say, on one big toe. It is generally agreed among neurophysiologists that, although impulses in the ingoing

[1] The Presidential Address to the Neurological Section of the Royal Society of Medicine, October, 1950, reprinted from *Brain*, 1950, **73**, 461.

nerves differ somewhat in their rates of conduction, there is no substantial difference between them corresponding to differences of sensory quality. The impulses in the optic nerve, auditory nerve and a sensory nerve from the skin, for example, are on the whole much the same. It is unlikely, therefore, that it is the character of the electrical impulse in the ingoing nerves which tells us that we are being touched, and there is certainly nothing toe-like in the impulses carried by the pathways conducting the sensations of touch from the toe which tells us that it is the toe which is being touched. No doubt, as Bishop[1] and le Gros Clark[2] point out, the fact that each sensory spot in the skin is supplied by branches of several nerve fibres conveys information of some localizing value, but it is information which must be interpreted centrally. The anatomist may be able to identify the toe area by tracing pathways of degeneration, the physiologist by detecting the response of the brain to peripheral stimulation, but this is information derived from the outside: both these external observers know to start with that the impulses come from the toe. The clinician and pathologist observe that a lesion in a certain area of the surface of the brain concerned with sensation causes a loss of feeling in the toe, but this does not explain why it should be so. If we imagine the nervous pathways from the toe to the brain completely isolated from the rest of the nervous system, it is clear that they could by themselves convey no localizing information, for how could electrical impulses exactly like those going to all the other sensory areas of the brain surface mean that something is happening to the toe? This surely provides a clue to the answer, which is that we can localize touch only by perceiving it in relation to a representation of the body as

[1] *Phys. Rep.*, 1946, **26**, 77.
[2] *Anatomical Pattern as the Essential Basis of Sensory Discrimination,* Oxford, 1947.

a whole—whether in the form of unconscious schema or fully conscious image is unimportant for our present purpose—and this body-schema maps out, as it were in a set of co-ordinates, all the possible voluntary actions which we should need to take in order to remove the stimulus either with the other foot or with either hand, or in any other way. Evidently, therefore, to perceive a part of the body as pricked is to perceive it in relationship with the whole of the rest of the body, pin-pointed, as it were, upon the body-image, and this process is something that happens to the raw material of the sensation of touch before it is presented to consciousness. Head, therefore, was wrong, as Walshe[1] has pointed out, in supposing that there is any distinct pathway for tactile localization in the spinal cord, for localization is something superimposed upon the appreciation of touch. It is possible as a result of a lesion of the brain surface for the patient to be aware of a touch without knowing where he has been touched, difficult though this is for the normal person to imagine. In other words, we can appreciate touch without knowing its whereabouts, but we cannot know a whereabouts that is vacant of any sensory content.

This process of localization of touch is a function of the surface of the brain, but if I am right in thinking that it relates the touch felt to the body-image as a whole, it must involve pathways far more extensive than the primary sensory areas for touch in the brain surface. When, therefore, the area corresponding to one great toe is excited by the arrival there of an afferent impulse resulting from stimulation of the toe itself, such excitation must cause a widespread irradiation of impulses linking the toe area with the areas which are concerned with awareness of the body-image, not only in the same half of the brain but also

[1] *Critical Studies in Neurology*, Edinburgh, 1948.

in the corresponding area on the opposite side. The same
thing must happen if the sensory area is excited by an
epileptic discharge or by an attack of migraine. The resulting hallucination of numbness referred to some part of the
body cannot be the result of a discharge limited to the part
stimulated. Paradoxically, in order that it may be localized,
it must irradiate to the anatomical basis of the body image.
And this, I take it, was what Hughlings Jackson[1] meant
when he said: 'I must submit that the units making up that
division of the highest centres which I call the anatomical
substrata of subject-consciousness represent (properly re-
represent) all parts of the body, mainly sensorily, in relation
to one another.' And again, speaking of a prick on the back,
'Physically, the nervous impulses starting from a point on
the periphery pricked "travel" to units of the highest centres
universally representing, and not to units representing one
part of the back only. . . . In general the anatomical substrata of subject-consciousness are centres of universal
co-ordination, or, as we said, they are unifying or synthe-
sizing centres.' Hence, when we speak of a part of the body
as being represented for purposes of sensation at a certain
point in a particular region of the brain on the opposite
side, we do not mean that the consciousness of a part of
the body is in some way localized there, but that the area in
question constitutes a nodal point at which the sensory
impulses coming from a particular part of the body are
brought into relation with the whole body-image by means
of pathways which must ramify widely throughout the
posterior halves of both cerebral hemispheres to reach
Jackson's division of the highest centres, the 'anatomical
substrata of subject-consciousness' representing all parts of
the body in relation to one another.

[1] *Selected Writings*, London, 1931, **2**, 96–7.

## IMAGERY AND MEMORY

A good deal has been written recently about disorders of the body-image itself and the main facts are now generally known. The most bizarre of these is the failure to attend to, or in extreme cases even to recognize as part of the body, the limbs on the left side as a result of a lesion in the posterior part of the right half of the brain. One such patient dried only the right side of the body when he had a bath. There is one important conclusion which, it seems to me, can be drawn from cases of this kind. The surprising thing about them is not that the patient should be unable to feel one-half of the body normally, but that he should apparently have forgotten that he ever possessed it. He not only disregards it but he does not know that he is disregarding it. We can miss something only if we can remember that we once had it. I conclude, therefore, that the lesion in such cases has destroyed not only the patient's present awareness of his body-image but also nerve-cells which are essential to his ability to remember that he ever possessed a left half of the body. If this is a true interpretation, it would seem that the process of remembering the body-image involves an activation of the same nerve-cells as are concerned in its current aware-ness, and this I suspect may be generally true. The remain-ing half of the bisected body-image seems to constitute itself a new Gestalt, and consciousness, having lost the memory of the left half of the body, is unaware of the incompleteness of what remains. The comment is often made that these patients, of course, are mentally abnormal, and this is sometimes put forward as an explanation of these peculiar psychophysiological phenomena, but this may be to invert cause and effect, for the body-image plays a very important part in our sense of identity, and a patient who has lost half of his body-image has suffered so severe a multilation of the psychophysiological basis of his ego that it is not surprising that he should become mentally disordered.

What happens in the brain when we exercise visual imagination, when we create a visual image of some past event or even of something purely imaginary? Electro-encephalography provides a clue in the fact that the exercise of the imagination interferes with the alpha rhythm, which is regarded as indicating a state of rest in the visual cortex. Grey Walter[1] concludes that 'this suggests that those cere-bral regions which were previously responding regularly to the external stimuli are mobilized for internal service when the attention is directed to an imaginary problem— it is possible, therefore, that imagination involves the projection of an internally constructed assembly of data upon the same area as is otherwise used for the processing of 'real' or external information before the pattern can be recognized and used for the miniature experiment of thought.' If this be true, isolated destruction of the whole visual cortex should destroy the capacity for visual imagery. Does this occur?

Lashley's[2] experiments with rats show that those animals which have been taught to find their way through a maze could still carry out this task after removal of any area of the brain except the parts directly concerned with vision. Moreover, Lashley has shown that when blind animals are trained in the maze the removal of the primary visual parts of the brain produces a severe loss of the habit with serious difficulty in relearning, although the animals could have used no visual cues in the initial learning. He suggests that 'a possible explanation of this curious effect was that the rat formed concepts of spatial relations in visual

[1] *J. Ment. Sci.*, 1950, **96**, 1.
[2] *J. Comp. Neurol.*, 1943, **79**, 431, and *Physiological Mechanisms in Animal Behaviour*, Cambridge, 1950, 454.

terms, as man seems to do, and that the space concepts are integrated in the visual cortex. The visual cortex might then function in the formation of spatial habits, even when the animal loses its sight.'

It sometimes happens that as a result of a lesion of the brain a patient loses all visual imagery, which can no longer be evoked voluntarily and ceases to occur spontaneously. This condition has also been called loss of revisualization. One such patient of mine showed a number of interesting features.

A man, aged 36, sustained a severe head injury with a depressed fracture in the mid-frontal region. When seen five years later his sole complaint was that he had 'lost his picture memory.' Previously a good visualizer, he could no longer visualize anything: he could not form a mental picture of people he knew intimately, but he could still recognize people, even when he had only seen them once before, and he could still describe people and objects even though he could no longer visualize them. He was a builder's manager, and he was still able to work, although, because he could no longer visualize a plan or an elevation, he had to keep referring to the specification. He built his own house by remodelling four cottages, and he would work out all the alterations on a plan at night, and would then inspect the work next day in order to correct any mistakes he had made in the plan. He could no longer picture routes, and, if going on a journey which he had travelled before, he had to look up maps and trace the route afresh. He still recognized landmarks when he came to them. He said that the character of his dreams had changed, a fact which he described as 'rather uncanny.' 'When I dream,' he said, 'I seem to know what is happening, but I don't seem then to see a picture. I can dream about a person without seeing him.' He could no longer visualize his own body. His only speech difficulty was concerned with spelling, which he attributed to an inability to visualize the words. His visual acuity and fields were normal.

In the case cited the functions preserved are as interesting as the functions lost. The patient could recognize objects normally, though he could no longer visualize them, and he could also describe them from memory. Thus, in his case at any rate, visual imagery played no part in visual recogni-

tion, and it is possible to have what I may term a propositional memory of things which cannot be visualized.
Here we have a very precise experiment on the value of
consciousness compared with unconscious mechanisms in
the visual sphere—a point to which I shall return.

Penfield's[1] observation that it was possible to evoke in a
patient an elaborate visual picture of a remembered scene
by electrical stimulation of the temporal lobe takes us a
step further towards the anatomy of memory. We seem
led to picture the anatomical basis of memory, so far as it
involves images, as innervating widespread areas of the
brain surface, including in all probability the relevant
primary sensory areas. Dreaming must involve in part the
same pathways. Clearly it would be quite erroneous to
picture either memories or images as 'stored' in some area
of the brain. We should think rather of a widespread net-
work of nerve-cells which can be set vibrating in an almost
infinite variety of patterns in space and time.

## CONSCIOUSNESS AND PATTERNS

One of the most fundamental properties of the brain is
that which renders possible the recognition of patterns.
The biological importance of this is obvious on a little reflec-
tion. Objects of the same kind differ among themselves.
Cats, for example, are not all alike. Survival, however,
often depends upon the ability of the organism to react to
all objects of a class in the same way. Clearly it would be
impossible for the nervous system to be so organized that
the appropriate reaction should be directly linked with each
group of stimuli representing each of the various individuals
of a given class. The organization required would be too
complex. Such reactions could not be innate nor could they

[1] *Proc. Roy. Soc. B.*, 1947, **124**, 329.

be learned by experience, because each fresh individual member of the group would constitute a new group of stimuli, the reaction to which had not previously been learned. If a mouse is to succeed in recognizing and reacting appropriately towards a cat, it must do so the first time or not at all, and it cannot afford to make the mistake of recognizing black cats as cats, but not white ones. The nervous system has solved this problem in what would seem to be the only possible way: it has introduced plasticity into the receptive side, so that what the animal reacts to is not a mosaic of all the individual features of the object perceived, but a pattern which constitutes an abstraction from any particular individual, but for that very reason is common to all individuals of the group. Thus, for example, a rat can be trained to recognize, in the sense of reacting in a trained manner to, triangles as distinct from other geometrical figures. Field experiments on the recognition of predatory birds by the small birds on which they prey (Hartley,[1] Lorenz,[2] Kratzig[3]) have shown that in several species the recognition of a hawk depends entirely upon the combination of two visual characters, outline and movement. A generalized silhouette has been produced which in birds, such as ptarmigan, causes fear reaction when moved in one direction, when it is, apparently, taken for the short-necked silhouette of a hawk, and no more than attention when moved in the other.

In this connection pattern is a general term of wide application and it usually stands for something much more complex than the instances which we have just considered. Thus, visual patterns may take into account not merely outline but also light and shade and, as we have seen, movement, and patterns can be discovered by other senses

[1] *Physiological Mechanisms in Animal Behaviour*, Cambridge, 1950, 313.
[2] *Verh. disch. zool. Ges.*, 1940, **1939**, 69 (quoted by Hartley).
[3] *J. Orn. Lpz.*, 1940, **88**, 139 (quoted by Hartley).

than vision: a musical tune, for example, is a pattern which is extended in time and which remains the same what ever its key and whatever the instrument on which it is played. As I have pointed out,[1] the recognition of words in speech involves an identical physiological process. We recognize a word when we hear it spoken by any person with whatever accent, at any pitch and whether shouted, whispered or sung. Similarly, we recognize it when we read it, whatever the size or character of the type in which it is printed and whether the print is coloured or black. In other words, we recognize a pattern which underlies all the auditory stimuli involved in uttering a particular word, though from a physical point of view and even from the point of view of stimuli which they produce in the auditory cortex they must in most respects be different from one another. In the same way we recognize some common patterns in all the visual representations of a single word. This process is unconscious, for there is no single group either of auditory or of visual stimuli into which we translate all the different ways of uttering or writing a word before we can understand it. The word, however expressed or written, is at once recognized as being the same word—as possessing, that is, the same meaning. So between various ways of expressing a word and our recognition that it is the same word with a single meaning there must exist a process in the nervous system which abstracts from the complex of the stimuli a pattern common to them all. And in man we can take the process much further, for not only is there such a pattern through which we recognize a word we hear and another pattern through which we recognize a word we see, and these in turn must submit to a similar process at a higher level, by which we reach a conception of the word as an element in thought, and words again are grouped

[1] *Perspectives in Neuropsychiatry*, London, 1950, 127.

into the patterns which constitute sentences, which underlie propositional speech; and it would seem that abstract thought itself need involve only the same physiological process at a higher level and in greater complexity.

Various views have been put forward (Lashley,[1] Brain[2]) as to what this process is. My own suggestion is that a modification of the concept of the schema put forward originally by Kant and introduced into neurology by Head and Holmes[3] is the key that fits the lock, and Pitts and McCulloch[4] have attempted to describe in mathematical terms the physiological processes in virtue of which the brain renders possible the recognition of universals. They claim no finality for their particular suggestion, but they have at least shown that, taking into account what is known of the structure and functions of the cerebral cortex, a plausible account can be given of the physiological process which is the foundation of much of our mental life, but which operates in such a way as to present to consciousness only the end-results of its activity.

## THE CEREBRAL BASIS OF FEELING

I have spoken earlier about the link between feeling and representation, and this is reflected in the impossibility of making a complete physiological and anatomical distinction between the functions of the cortex and those of the dien-cephalon. When we react emotionally either to the per-ception of objects or to the contemplation of an idea there must be impulses passing between the surface and deeper parts of the brain (the diencephalon and hypothalamus). We are still far from understanding the physiology of

[1] *Biol. Sympos.*, 1942, **7**, 301.
[2] *Perspectives in Neuropsychiatry*, London, 1950, 127.
[3] *Studies in Neurology*, London, 1920, **2**, 605.
[4] *Bull. Math., Physics*, 1947, **9**, 127.

their mutual relationship. Nevertheless, I think that Head and Holmes were right in maintaining that the conscious experiences which we call feelings are correlated with these deeper nuclei, particularly the optic thalamus, in the sense that we experience feelings when nervous impulses reach these parts of the brain. In the realm of feelings it is useful to distinguish those which are localized in some part of the body, such as pain, and which are termed sensations, and those which are not so localized and which are termed emotions. I experience pain in some part of my body, but I do not experience joy anywhere in particular. A parallel distinction can be made in the functions of the brain surface for I localize my perception both of the external world and of my body, but I do not localize my thoughts.

## THE BIOLOGY OF CONSCIOUSNESS

Let us now take a few steps back from this unfinished picture and see how it looks from a biological standpoint. Whether or not the behaviour of any organism which possesses a nervous system can be explained entirely in terms of reflex action, there can be no doubt that organisms with the most primitive types of nervous system exhibit mainly the characteristics which we have come to associate with the simpler types of reflex action, similar in essentials to those studied by Sherrington in the spinal cord of the dog. Of these I would stress two. The first is the inevitability or automaticity of response. This, of course, does not mean that the same stimulus always produces exactly the same effect, for the response is modified by the state of the rest of the nervous system at the time at which it is applied, but within these limits the response to the stimulus is automatic. Secondly, both the stimulus and the response are immediate. When we think of such reflexes we picture some kind of stimulus applied directly to the organism, as when salivation is produced by placing meat in a dog's mouth, or blinking occurs on touching the surface of the eye. Even when a distance-receptor, such as the eye, is the afferent channel, as in the light reflex, we tend to think of the effective stimulus as the light falling upon the eye rather than the torch or other source of illumination in the distance. It is only in the more highly evolved animals that distance-receptors come to assume importance as reflex channels. In the case of the primitive reflex in the primitive organism the stimulus is immediate in the sense that it is not mediated; that is, it is a direct contact with some part of the animal's body. The response is similarly immediate or practically so: there is no long delay between the arrival of the stimulus and the reaction of the effector organ.

We do not know whether reflex activity is ever directly related to consciousness. We are familiar with many reflexes in ourselves of which we are quite unconscious, though consciousness may be superimposed, as when we feel the touch on the cornea which causes an involuntary closure of the eye, but it is clear that consciousness could add nothing to a reaction which is the inevitable response to a stimulus.

One of the great advances in evolution was the development of what Sherrington has called distance-receptors; that is, the receptors reacting to objects at a distance. Sherrington[1] says: 'The "distance-receptors" seem to have peculiar importance for the construction and evolution of the nervous system. In the higher grades of the animal scale one part of the nervous system has, as Gaskell insists, evolved with singular constancy a dominant importance to the individual. That is the part which is called the brain. The brain is always the part of the nervous system which is

[1] *The Integrative Action of the Nervous System*, 2nd Ed., Cambridge, 1947, 325.

D

constructed upon and evolved upon the "distance-receptor" organs.' The development of distance-receptors had a profound effect upon the organism's relationship not only to space but also to time. If it is to react to objects at a distance, time must enter into the organization of its nervous system in a manner which has no parallel in the more primitive creature which responds automatically to immediate stimuli. The organism which is to react to an object at a distance must initiate a course of action which takes time, whether it is to go in pursuit of it or endeavour to avoid it. No doubt in the lowliest organisms with distance-receptors the times concerned are not very long. Nevertheless, as soon as reactions evolved which were organized in time and directed towards objects continuing in time, the nervous system came to possess potentially a type of reaction which was capable of maintaining a specific activity for an indefinitely extended length of time.

How was this done? By the development of new types of nervous function, which, though we consider them separately, are so closely integrated in action that their separation is to some extent an artificial abstraction. The first is feeling. We can, of course, know nothing about any feelings except those of human beings, our own by direct awareness and other people's by what they can tell us about them. From our own experience it seems clear that our feelings either themselves provide the motive power, or, if you prefer the term, are the manifestations in consciousness of the motive power, which sustains our courses of action in time. The time concerned may be short, as when hunger sends us in search of a meal, or indefinitely protracted as when an interest in scientific research determines the activities of a life-time. Any interpretation of animal behaviour in terms of human consciousness must be made with caution. Nevertheless, there is far less difference between a higher animal and man in respect of the deeper structures which we believe to be the basis of feeling than there is in respect of development of the brain surface. Therefore, having regard to the principle of evolution, it seems likely that animals experience feelings which are associated with impulses to action, whether these are comparatively short-term activities, like the pursuit of prey or the escape from an enemy, or more lengthy and elaborate proceedings, such as those concerned with the care of the young.

But, as we have just seen, feeling is directed towards an object, and if actions are to take time the organism must possess an enduring representation of that object. Here we reach the other new function of the nervous system, the representation of the external world. I do not propose to discuss the philosophical aspects of consciousness but probably most, if not all, neurologists accept what has been called 'physiological idealism.' All that we know about the physiology of the conduction of nervous impulses teaches us that perception only occurs when nervous impulses reach the appropriate end-stations in the brain, that these nervous impulses are all much alike and that they are quite unlike the physical stimuli whether of light, sound or chemical character which initiate them. Our perceptions, therefore, are largely a product of the activity of our nervous systems and they are, as we say, 'projected,' and perceived as being external to ourselves. This, of course, has given rise to a number of philosophical puzzles, with which we are not now concerned, but, if you accept physiological idealism, you will be prepared to agree that the world which we perceive is a representation of the outer world created to a large extent by the nervous system, and this I would suggest is the function of the brain surface on its receptive side.

We can go further, for if at least what the philosophers

call secondary qualities, such as smells, sounds, colours and so on, are quite unlike the physical stimuli which give rise to them, then we must regard them as symbols of physical reality and say that the receptive function of the cerebral cortex is to provide us with a symbolical representation of the whole of the external world, not only distinguishing objects by their qualities, but also conveying to us the spatial relationships which exist between them, and at the same time giving us similar symbolical information about our own bodies and their relationship with the external world. All this information, of course, is given us not merely for the sake of pure awareness or contemplation, though that may sometimes be a by-product of it, but in order that we may act; hence it is linked, in ways with which we are familiar, with the motor activities of the brain. This is the element in consciousness which for convenience of brevity we may call 'cortical' (that is, a function of the brain surface). My patient who had lost his powers of visual imagery illustrates very well the normal contribution of imagery to action in providing an enduring model of the external world.

As soon as the nervous system had acquired the power to create representations of the external world the potentiality of memory made its appearance. Learning is within the capacity of extremely primitive organisms and it is certainly possible that it may occur in the absence of any representation of the external world, by some process of facilitation of repeated reactions, but it seems impossible that we should remember something of which we have not previously experienced a representation.

If all perception is a symbolic representation, it follows that symbolization is an inherent function of the nervous system, and there is no difficulty in understanding the further step by which a hierarchy of symbolic processes occurs.

Thus, all speech and thought which employ symbols to represent perceptual experiences or ideas are merely a further development of the symbolizing function of the nervous system. We should be wrong if we regarded such higher types of symbolization as peculiar to man. The remarkable observations of von Frisch on the honey-bee, reviewed and confirmed by Thorpe,[1] show that the worker on returning to the hive indicates to other workers a new source of food by means of a dance in which 'the direction of action of gravity is symbolic of the direction of incidence of the sun's rays.'

[1] *Physiological Mechanisms in Animal Behaviour*, Cambridge, 1950, 387.

# IV

# THE INTERVENTION OF THE
# NERVOUS SYSTEM

THE problem of mind and matter has been discussed for over 2,000 years, but it seems timely to look at the question again in the light of two developments of thought during the last twenty-five years which have contributed to put it in a new light. The first is the great increase in our knowledge of neurophysiology and especially of the electrophysiology of the nervous system. The second is the contribution of those philosophers who are particularly concerned with semantics. They may often go too far in supposing that problems are purely verbal, but they have rendered a great service by directing our attention to the large part which verbal confusions play in creating difficulties, and have thereby clarified our thought. That they have not achieved more is, I think, due to the fact that with the notable exceptions of Eddington, Whitehead and Russell no modern philosopher seems aware of the importance of the part played by the body in perception and thought, and current philosophies of perception either dispose of such questions as merely verbal or are satisfied with very naïve armchair solutions.

Before I go further, let me add two words of explanation. This is at best a difficult subject and I believe that if we are to understand even how the difficulties arise we must depart somewhat from the time-worn paths of approach. Secondly, in a broad survey such as I am now attempting there will not be time to discuss every point in detail, to deal with the history of the subject or to counter opposing arguments. To some extent I can only present conclusions, but I hope to be able to make clear how they have been reached.

Let us begin by considering the use of the words 'mind' and 'matter.' Evidently people think that they mean something when they use these words, and they do not think that they are in the habit of using them for the same events. Going no deeper than the verbal level, if the distinction between the words 'mind' and 'matter' means anything we should try to understand what it means, and if it does not mean anything we should be clear about that also.

Philosophers and other thinking people who have assumed that there is some distinction between mind and matter have been chiefly concerned with two different questions: (1) What is the relationship between those events we call mental and the collection of matter which we call our brains? and (2), Are the things which we perceive with our senses wholly material or, as some have thought, wholly mental, or partly one and partly the other? As we shall see, these questions are intimately related to one another.

People sometimes put it in this way: 'Is matter *really* mental?' or 'Is the mind *really* a manifestation of the matter of which the brain is composed?' Evidently there is something which they mean by matter which, at first sight at any rate, is different from mind, and conversely—whatever these two terms may turn out to represent when we get to know more about them.

Let us, without attempting to define matter, look at some instances of the use of the term. If we ask someone to give us some examples of matter he might say that it consists of solids, liquids and gases, or that it exists in the form of tables and chairs, muscles and bones, nerves and brains.

If we then say: 'What do you mean by the mind, or what would you regard as mental?' he might find it more difficult to reply. Thought would certainly seem to be mental, for thinking is perhaps the most characteristic function of the mind, as we use the term. Feeling and willing? Yes, those would probably also be regarded as mental. But what about sensation? Is there something mental about colours, touches and sounds? Here we should begin to get into a difficulty; in fact, we should find ourselves at once involved in the ancient controversy between the idealist and the realist. On the one hand, if we regard sensations as a state of consciousness and assume that the mind is somehow involved in consciousness, we can make out a case for treating them as mental; but on the other hand, the colour of the table certainly seems to be in some way part of the table, though the sound of a bell is not in quite the same way part of the bell and a touch on my hand appears to come into yet another category, because it is not exactly part of the object touching me nor can it be described as part of my hand.

Instead of talking about isolated sensations let us think of a solid object which I hold in my hand. I perceive that object through touches and pressures, and feelings of heat or cold, together with information derived from the posture of my fingers and the extent to which they are separated by the object from the palm of my hand. Are all these sensations mental or are they part of the object? If I feel that a stone in my hand is cold I do so only because it causes a fall of temperature in my skin which makes my fingers colder than they were and excites certain nerve-endings. Yet I usually speak of the stone and not of my hand as being cold, though I can remember a small child putting his hand in the river and saying, 'I am going to feel my hand in the water.'

Let us leave this question on one side for the moment and turn now to what we call the world of matter. How do we know about the tables and chairs, about other people's bodies and brains and, for that matter, about our own bodies and brains? Let us see what happens when somebody else, whom we will call the observer, sees a colour or hears a sound.

The physical stimulus, as we call it, excites the appropriate receptor organ, in this case the eye or ear, and this in turn starts an electrical impulse in the corresponding nerve running to the brain. These nerve-impulses differ somewhat in minor details, including the rate at which they are conducted towards the central nervous system, but they are substantially alike, and no neurophysiologist believes that differences in the nature of the impulses conducted by the ingoing nerves correspond to differences in the kind of sensation which they lead us to experience. Thus merely from recording the electrical disturbances which accompany the passage of a nerve-impulse and observing their characteristics it is impossible to say whether the sensation with which they are concerned is one of sight, hearing, sound, taste or touch, and, indeed, it is not until such nerve-impulses reach what may be called their end-stations in the brain that we experience a sensation at all. It would seem, therefore, that what determines our awareness of a sensation, and also its nature, is the arrival of a nerve-impulse, or more probably a series of nerve-impulses, at the appropriate end-station in the brain.

We have other evidence in support of this view, for clinical neurology teaches us that we can experience a sensation without any sensory organs being excited, and without any impulse travelling up an ingoing nerve. All that is necessary is that the appropriate area of brain should be excited in some other way. Thus we know that if one of the end-stations of the brain normally concerned with sensation is stimulated by the electrical discharge which underlies an epileptic fit, or by the disturbance which constitutes an attack of migraine, the patient will experience a sensation corresponding in quality to the area of brain excited, and we know further that a very wide range of sensations, including sight, smell, sound, taste, touch and others, can all be reproduced by exciting the appropriate area of the cortex, some of them even by the surgeon using an electrical stimulus on the conscious patient. It is true that the sensations produced in this way are usually of a some- what crude kind, but then the stimulus is of a crude kind, and, when once the principle has been accepted that the application to the brain of a stimulus which is capable of evoking a response will produce a sensation, there is no reason to doubt that if we were able to deliver a more refined and complicated stimulus, complicated in its organization both in space and time, we could reproduce more complex kinds of sensation.

What follows from this? We have seen that a physical stimulus excites a sensory receiving-organ, and this a nerve- impulse, which is in no way like the original physical stimulus and that this in turn sets going a disturbance in the end-station in the brain which is probably in certain respects unlike the nerve-impulse, and certainly is quite unlike the original physical stimulus, and it is upon this disturbance in the brain that sensation depends. Hence the brain state which constitutes the physical basis of a sensation is always quite unlike the physical stimulus which impinges upon the body and which has been in one way or another directly set in motion by the external object which we experience. Thus the relationship between the brain state which underlies the sensation and the physical object of which that sensation makes us aware is merely that the brain state is the last of a series of events caused by the physical stimulus. Whatever the relationship between the brain state underlying a sensation and the corresponding awareness of the sensation in consciousness it would seem to follow that the sensation must be quite unlike the physical stimulus originating in the outside world and exciting the sense-organs.

It follows also that the experience of a given sensation must always be later in time than the physical event which initiates it. Indeed, it must be later in time than the excitation of the receptors on the surface of the body by that physical event, since the nerve-impulse takes time to travel from the surface of the body to the brain. How much later in time it is than the physical event will depend obviously upon the distance of the object concerned from the body and the rate of propagation of the physical stimulus through the intervening medium. The speed of light is so great that only a fraction of a second intervenes between the time when a light wave is reflected from any object on the earth and the time when it strikes the eye of the observer. This interval is so short that for all practical purposes it can be neglected, and we normally pay no attention to it. We behave as though we see something happening at the very moment at which it happens. We cannot do this, however, in the sphere of astronomy where years may pass between the moment at which a light wave leaves a star and that at which the eye perceives it. If it takes several years for the light from a star at which I am now looking to reach my eye, the star can no longer be in the position at which I see it, and, indeed, if it had ceased to exist in the interval between the present moment and that at which the light wave left it I should have no means of discovering the fact. Owing to the relatively slow speed of sound compared with that of light this anomaly may become obvious

even on the surface of the earth when sound is concerned.
The sound of a jet-plane comes from a different point in
the sky from that at which we see the plane.

So we reach the idea that the only necessary condition of
the observer's seeing colours, hearing sounds and experiencing his own body is that the appropriate physiological
events shall occur in the appropriate areas of his brain. If
these are of the right kind the same sensory experience will
occur irrespective of whether they are caused solely by a
local change in the brain, or by a long chain of events
originating in the external world. But if we ask the
observer where the events he is experiencing are, where he
sees the colours, hears the sounds or feels part of his body,
he does not point to his brain, he points to or describes
some region of the external world or some part of his body
itself external to his brain, and he does the same whether
his sensations are produced normally (that is, by events
external to his brain) or abnormally (that is, by disease
processes occurring in his brain itself).

Here, then, is a problem. An event in the observer's brain
causes him to experience something; for example, see a colour
outside his brain. This is what neurologists and psycholo-
gists often call 'projection,' but this is not a very good name
for it, for projection seems to imply throwing something
from one place to another, but the colour the observer sees
is never anywhere else but where he sees it. He is not aware
of any process that could rightly be called projection.

Now let us look at the external world as the observer
perceives it. It is hard or soft, coloured, scented, tasty,
and composed of objects which have position and may
move about. As we have seen, the time-relationships of
the observer's external world are peculiar. If an event in it
causes a sound, he hears it, not when the event occurs, but
when the sound, as we say, reaches his ear, or, more

precisely, a little later, when the nerve-impulse from his ear has travelled as far as the part of his brain surface concerned with hearing. Similarly, he sees an object, not when the light wave leaves it, but when the visual nerve-impulse has reached his brain, and in the astronomical world this may be a thousand years after the event which originates the light wave.

Consider two stars, one 500 and one 1,000 light years away: the observer sees them both at the same time, but the events he perceives on the stars (that is, the emission of light waves) happened 500 years apart. So events which the observer perceives simultaneously are not necessarily simultaneous. In fact, the observer's perceptual view consists of events which stretch away into the past in proportion as they are distant from him in space, but which are on one time-scale for vision and another for hearing, in proportion to the differences between the speeds of sound and of light.

What about the body? Surely we have a direct and immediate awareness of that? No, the same principle applies. All the observer's perception of his own body is awareness of its immediate past, for he is not aware of the prick of a pin until after the interval of time necessary for a nerve-impulse to travel to his brain from the part of the body which has been pricked.

# V

## THE TWO 'WORLDS'

WE left the observer at the end of the last chapter making
the discovery that he has to deal with two 'worlds'—as we
may call them for the moment. There is the 'world' of
his perceptions and another 'world' which differs from the
'world' he perceives in various respects, one of the most
important of which is that events in this other 'world'
occur at different times from those at which the observer
perceives them. There is one exception to this—his brain
—but here we are dealing with a correlation of a different
order, for though it is probably true to say that when an
event in the observer's brain causes him to experience something, the two occurrences, the brain event and his
experience, are simultaneous, yet in such circumstances the
observer is never aware of an event in his brain, but of an
event somewhere else. I propose for the moment to
distinguish these two 'worlds' which exist in relation to
the observer by calling them the perceptual 'world' and
the physical 'world.'

But, you will say, if the observer's knowledge of any
'world' is limited to his perceptions, how does he ever
discover that there is any other 'world'? He does so by a
process of inference operating in two ways.

(i) He accepts the observations of other people. Almost
the whole of our knowledge of the correlation between
sensation and brain function comes to us in this way. We
stimulate the brain and ask the patient for his sensations,
or we ask about sensations and the effects produced upon

them by disease and then study the brain after death. But we can use the sensations of other people in another way; for example, by using another person as an observer of an event and comparing his observations with our own.

(ii) The observer can himself carry out experimental observations. In practice he profits by the observations of scientists, but they are of a kind which given the requisite apparatus and skill he could carry out for himself—for example, he sees a man hitting something with a hammer; he walks away and notices that he hears each blow at an increasing interval after he sees it occur. From this he infers the speed of sound. Complex physical apparatus enables physicists to infer the speed of light. It follows that from the 'world' we perceive we are able to infer a 'world' of events of which we are not able to have any more direct knowledge.

Each of us has his own perceptual 'world.' Your 'world' and mine are different both in time and in content. If you stand half-way between me and a source of sound you hear the sound at a different time from me; hence your perceptual 'world' contains a sound when mine does not, and vice versa. Similarly, another person's perceptual 'world' may contain a phantom limb or a toothache, which I cannot perceive. But if our inferences are made according to the appropriate rules we shall all agree about the physical 'world.'

At this point let us pause to see how philosophical problems may arise out of verbal confusions in describing the facts of which I have just given an account.

One source of confusion is due to the fact that we do not in everyday life need to discriminate between our own perceptual 'worlds' and the physical 'world.' When I see a table, I do not distinguish a perceptual table from a physical table, nor when I speak of a table do I need to specify whether I am referring to one or the other or both. In fact,

I pass from one to the other and use the same term for both indifferently.

Now we have seen that your perceptual 'world' and my perceptual 'world' are entirely distinct, but that we share the same physical 'world,' so when you and I talk about a table, all goes well as long as it is not necessary to distinguish between them. But suppose that an observer suffers from hallucinations and declares that he sees a table when neither I nor anyone else can see one. It is useless to try and persuade him that he is not seeing a table because his experience is the same as when he has seen a table in the past. In other words, there exists a table in his perceptual 'world,' but there is no table in the physical 'world' in the appropriate situation, and therefore there is no table, corresponding to the table in his perceptual 'world,' in the perceptual 'world' of any normal person. In other words, the table in his perceptual 'world' is not caused by a physical table but by something else, and normally a table in the perceptual 'world' *is* caused by a physical table.

The great neurologist Hughlings Jackson made this point very clearly when he described a patient who was a cabman and who thought that his bed was a cab. Hughlings Jackson[1] said: 'This patient saw a cab, had that image strongly "projected," his objective state, at a time when I saw a bed, when I had that image strongly "projected," my objective state. It is of no avail for trustworthy witnesses to assert that the patient "*could not have seen*" a cab, because there is no cab present, and therefore, that the patient "only fancied," etc., that he saw one. Something, not himself, "got out of" himself the image cab, "out of" the bystander the image bed. It might be said that this doctrine confuses reality and unreality. But what reality

[1] *Selected Writings*, London, 1931, **1**, 384.

and whose reality? The image cab was the patient's reality; the image bed was the healthy bystander's reality.'

The age-long controversy between the realist and the idealist in the sphere of perception is greatly simplified if we realize the part which words play in it. If we ask whether the colour of a table is part of the table the answer is 'Yes' if by table we mean the table in the perceptual 'world' which belongs to each of us, but it is 'No' if we mean the table in the physical 'world' which is common to all of us. Let us suppose that I see a table, decide that it is in the wrong place, and proceed to move it. It is true to say that in this process I am aware of what are sometimes called sense-data; that is to say, colours, touches, pressures and so on. It is also true to say that I perceive a physical table. We should normally prefer to say that I moved the table rather than that I moved my sense-data, but that is a matter of usage. We have, in fact, two different ways of describing the same events. No difficulty will arise as long as we remember this, but there will be much confusion if we use the two methods indiscriminately.

What, then, is the relationship between them? What is the connection between what I have called a table in my perceptual 'world' and a table in the physical 'world'? The answer, I think, is, as I have suggested in more detail in Chapter III, that 'if at least what the philosophers call secondary qualities, such as smells, sounds, colours and so on, are quite unlike the physical stimuli which give rise to them, then we must regard them as symbols of physical reality and say that the receptive function of the brain is to provide us with a symbolical representation of the physical world outside it, not only distinguishing objects by their qualities, but also conveying to us the spatial relationships which exist between them, and at the same time giving us

E

similar symbolical information about our own bodies and
their relation to the external world.'

Let us apply these ideas to the simple experience of seeing
a red light. Making use of conceptual symbols I say that
waves of a certain wave length and frequency start at a
certain spot and pass through space to the retinae of my
eyes, there initiating a series of impulses of quite different
frequency which pass along the visual pathways of my
nervous system and set up a disturbance in the parts of my
brain concerned with vision. I then see the red light.
The red light in my perceptual 'world' is a symbolical
representation of the events in the physical 'world' of which
a certain wave-length and frequency are the conceptual
symbols, but the events in my brain which cause me to see
the red light are quite different from red light as the physicist
knows it. My perceptual 'world,' therefore, is a kind of map.
It is not identical with the physical 'world' any more than a
map is identical with the country which it represents,
but it is able to symbolize it because events in my perceptual
'world' stand for events in the physical 'world.'

To some people this idea is difficult because our representation of the physical 'world' is a three-dimensional one, and
they find it hard to understand how each of us can have
his own three-dimensional perceptual 'world' which is yet
different from the three-dimensional physical 'world.' It
may make this idea easier to grasp if we go back to our
analogy of the map. It is true that an ordinary map represents in two dimensions something which exists in three.
Nevertheless, a map is really a structure in three dimensions
since it must have some degree of thickness and you can
easily have a map in which a third dimension is represented
arbitrarily but conventionally by lines or colours which stand
for the contour. But let me extend the analogy. Suppose
that instead of a map we have a globe. Here is a symbolical

representation of the whole world in three dimensions with a diameter of a few inches or one or two feet. There can be hundreds or thousands of such globes, each of them representing the earth, and there will be plenty of room for them all within the real earth. Now, each of our individual perceptual 'worlds' possesses a physical basis in the physical 'world'; namely, the brain. The perceptual 'world' depends upon complicated events occurring in the brain and caused by other events in the physical 'world.' The physical events in each physical brain, therefore, underlie for each of us our three-dimensional map of the physical 'world.' There is plenty of room in the physical 'world' for any number of brains, each of which acts as a basis of one of its representations, just as there is plenty of room in the physical earth for any number of globes each of which acts as one of its models. And there is plenty of room for the perceptual 'worlds' since, though each of these represents the physical 'world' in its entirety, it takes up no more room in it than is occupied by its physical basis in the brain.

Now we are in a position to see how the idea of the 'projection' of colours, sounds and touches on to the external world arises and how it can be explained. We know from the study of physiology and psychology and of the effects of disease of the brain that simplest brain-event concerned with sensation never occurs in isolation. The nervous system is in constant activity and nerve-impulses are continuously streaming into it from all parts of the body conveying to it 'information' about the position of the body in space and of the various parts of the body in relation to one another. Some of these impulses reach consciousness in the form of direct awareness—'items of information,' as it were: others never reach consciousness individually but contribute to the meaning of other items of consciousness. Hence, normally a touch on the hand or the sight of a colour does not merely excite the appropriate area of brain concerned with its own form of sensation: it fits into an elaborate pattern of electrical impulses in many parts of the brain. In terms of consciousness, when we say 'I feel a touch' or 'I see a light' we are isolating, for descriptive purposes, what is in the focus of consciousness and neglecting not only the background of experience against which we perceive it but necessarily also the unconscious contributions which the nervous system makes to its meaning. What we perceive is thus always perceived *in relation to* the rest of the body and this in turn *in relation to* other objects in space. One of the relationships of which we are thus aware is the relationship of externality. The electrical patterns of the nervous system convey to us the information that my hand and my foot are in different positions (that is, as parts of my body they are external to one another) and similarly that the table which I see is in a different position to my body (that is, external to it).

The confusion about 'projection,' the mysterious displacement of sensations from my brain to the external world arises from the fact that there are two meanings of the word 'external' just as there are two meanings of the word 'table,' and they refer to the two 'worlds' we have already distinguished. Let me try to make this clear by returning to the analogy of the map. Suppose I am sitting in London and have a map of England before me. On the map I see both London and Oxford, and I note that Oxford is external to London on the map just as it is in the physical world. But because the map which contains Oxford is itself in London, am I right in saying that Oxford is in London and is somehow 'projected' outside it? Confusion does not arise in this instance because we have been brought up to recognize the symbolical nature of a map, and we know that we are using the words Oxford and London

differently in the two cases, in the one instance to refer
directly to places in the physical world, in the other instance
to refer indirectly to marks on a map which themselves
refer to places in the physical world and the relationship
between them. Just so, when I say I see a table external to
my body I am talking of perceptual symbols representing
objects in the physical 'world' and their mutual relationship.
The physical basis of these symbols exists in my physical
brain, but if I say that my sensations are projected outside
my body I am confusing externality in the perceptual
'world' with externality in the physical 'world.'

Now let me try to clarify the conclusions we have
reached so far. I have spoken of two 'worlds'—in inverted
commas—but, of course, there is only one world—without
inverted commas—which from one point of view consists
of physical events including the events in our brains. The
combination of our sense-organs and the nervous system
when stimulated by the impact of physical impulses coming
from outside has the peculiar property of creating in various
ways symbolical representations of the rest of the world.
Each of these symbolical representations is in its totality
private to the observer whose consciousness is related to
each particular nervous system. For the sake of convenience
we often speak of this perceptual representation also as 'the
world.' This is as valid as it is to speak of John's photograph
as John, but many philosophical confusions have arisen
as a result of a failure to distinguish between the world and
its representation, because so often it seems natural to use
the same term for both.

# VI

# SYMBOLS AND PATTERNS

EXPERIENCE and our reflections upon it have led us to the distinction between the physical 'world' on the one hand and its perceptual representation on the other. The physical 'world' consists of the subject matter of physics and corresponds in general to what people loosely term matter. Perceptual representation must have a good deal in common with the physical 'world'—for example, up to a point structural correspondence—but it also includes much, such as its sensory qualities, which so far have no counterpart in physics. The physical 'world' is common to all observers: the perceptual representation of it is private and subjective. There are also other events which are private and subjective and seem to have much in common with perceptual representation; for example, our feelings and our thoughts. Many people would apply the term 'mind' or 'mental' to some at any rate of these subjective events. They would probably agree that thinking is mental and possibly, also, feeling, but there would be more difficulty in deciding about sensation. It is important to recognize that the one feature which all these subjective states have in common is that they are actually or potentially conscious, and the question we should next consider is what is the relationship between any of these conscious states, such as sensations, feelings, and thoughts and their physical basis in the brain. Here we seem confronted with two main alternatives. We can either take the view that conscious states are not identical with physical brain-states. They may be parallel with them, or caused by them, the result of interaction between brain states and something else, but they are not the same. Alternatively, we can conclude that we are dealing with events of only one kind. What we call events in the physical brain are happenings about which we may have indirect knowledge inferred from our perception of other people's brains and what they tell us about their experiences, but we have direct awareness of the physical events in our own brains and when we thus experience them we find them to be sensations, feelings and other conscious states.

Let us consider the arguments for and against these two views. The chief argument in favour of the view that brain events and conscious states are two aspects of the same happenings is that the correlation between the two is so close that we have no reason to suppose the occurrence of one without the other, and, that being so, it is a simpler and more economical hypothesis to believe that the distinction is created by our mode of thought. The arguments for dualism are negative in character. There appears to be nothing in the account which physiology gives of the nervous system which can enable us to translate brain events into states of consciousness. As Dr. Johnson[1] put it long ago, 'matter can differ from matter only in form, density, bulk, motion and direction of motion: to which of these however varied or combined can consciousness be annexed?' Again, Sherrington[2] writes: 'The search in that (energy) scheme for a scale of equivalence between energy and mental experience arrives at none. . . . The two, for all I can do, remain refractorily apart. They seem to me disparate; not mutually convertible, untranslatable the one into the other.' Brain-states consist, neurophysiology tells us, of rapidly moving changes of electrical potential in highly complex chemical structures; how can these, however we

---

[1] *The History of Rasselas, Prince of Abissinia*, London, 1759.
[2] *Man on his Nature*, Cambridge, 1940.

look at them, ever be identified with sights and sounds, hopes and fears, falling in love and discussing the nature of the mind?

Let me here point out that the difficulty upon which the dualists lay such stress exists for them in just as tough a form. For there is no doubt that changes in the physiology of the brain produce parallel and proportionate changes in consciousness. It is certainly difficult to see how a pattern of electrical impulses can *be* a pain; but it is equally inexplicable how, if a pain is a state of an independent mind, it can be changed in quality by a lesion of a peripheral nerve or of the brain itself. The problem of the influence of nervous structure upon consciousness remains, whether it is supposed to be immediate or exerted at one remove upon an intangible mind.

I want now to draw attention to the bearing of certain psychophysiological facts upon this and then to suggest that it looks somewhat less formidable from the philosophical standpoint I adopted in the earlier part of this chapter. I have just mentioned pain. Can we imagine how the passage of electrical impulses along certain nerve fibres to an end-station in the brain can result in a sensation of pain? There is evidence that it is impossible to stimulate a single pain fibre, so that even from the periphery a relationship between several fibres conducting impulses is involved in the simplest sensation. There is also evidence that an alteration in the number of pain fibres, either in the peripheral nerves, or in the pathways in the spinal cord, or in the brain itself, substantially affects the quality of the pain which is experienced. Thus, it could seem that pain is the state of consciousness which corresponds to a certain pattern of nerve-impulses existing in space and time. There is evidence, too, that patterns play an integral part in our recognition of objects, in our understanding of words and sentences and in our comprehension of ideas.

But, you may rightly object, granting all this, granting that patterns of brain-activity in space and time play an essential part in making mental processes possible, the gulf between patterns of electrical impulses and the richness and variety of states of consciousness is as wide as ever. In the earlier chapters I drew attention to what I called the two kinds of 'world,' the perceptual 'world' and the physical 'world,' but I said that of course there is really only one world. Now for the two kinds of world let me substitute two kinds of knowledge of the single world. There is knowledge depending upon perceptual symbols, aroused by stimuli reaching the body from outside itself, and which we call perception, and there is knowledge by means of conceptual symbols derived from perception by a process of inference. Our knowledge of what I have called the physical world is of the second kind. When, therefore, we ask how a pattern of electrical impulses in the brain can *be* a colour, what we are really saying is: 'How can events for which we use conceptual symbols involving electricity be represented also by the perceptual symbol of colour?' To be puzzled by this is logically very like asking: 'How on earth can a man called William have a moustache?' The analogy, I admit, is not quite perfect, because there is normally no connection between being called William and having a moustache, and there is some connection between neurophysiological patterns in the brain and colours, but in the present state of our knowledge there is no explainable relationship between the conceptual and perceptual symbols which respectively represent them.

The view which I have been putting forward has many important and interesting implications.

If the perceptual world of each of us is to represent the

physical world, certain features must be common to both: broadly speaking, the perceptual world must reproduce the structure of the physical world. In addition, the perceptual world contains features which are purely subjective, however external and independent of the observer they seem to be. It is, in fact, the product of a fusion between subjective and objective elements, a fact which is of great importance in our understanding of animism, magic and art. The qualities with which the savage endows places and objects really belong to them, not in the sense that they are qualities of those objects in the physical world but that they are part of the objects in his perceptual world, because this is to some extent part of himself.

The same is true of art. When an artist represents an object, as in painting a landscape or a portrait, he does not merely reproduce the pattern of sensory impressions it produces in him, but that pattern as modified by his own feelings and thoughts. Such a picture is never just a representation of reality: it is a distortion created by the passage of the sensory impressions through the magnetic field of the artist's personality, and this is literally true, since we can regard the artist's personality in neurophysiological terms as the resultant of the extremely complex electrical forces of his brain. 'I never saw a sunset like that, Mr. Turner,' said the lady. 'Don't you wish you could, Madam?' replied Turner. But when we see a sunset the result is not just a sunset, it is a sunset plus something in us. And a sunset plus Turner's lady questioner did not equal a sunset plus Turner. 'A fool,' says Blake, 'sees not the same tree that a wise man sees,' which is literally true.

The subjective element is even more prominent in abstract or non-representational art, in which, as Herbert Read[1] puts it, 'feeling is contemplated, but not within a philo-

---

[1] *The Meaning of Art*, Penguin Books, London, 1950, 164.

sophical frame of reference which lays down what the world is, or what it should be.' Herbert Read[1] quotes Tolstoy's definition of art:

'To evoke in oneself a feeling one has experienced, and having evoked it in oneself, then by means of movement, lines, colours, sounds, or forms expressed in words so to transmit that feeling that others experience the same feeling —this is the activity of art.

'Art is a human activity consisting in this, that one man consciously, by means of certain external signs, hands on to others feelings he has lived through, and that others are infected by these feelings and also experience them.'

This is the expression in psychological terms of the process which I have been describing in terms of neurophysiology. Each account is valid in its own sphere and they illuminate each other, provided each takes its proper place in a theory of knowledge which can find room for both.

What kind of world do we find ourselves in if the ideas I have been discussing are true? First, what is the distinction between mind and matter? This is, more perhaps than we have been accustomed to think, a question of terminology. If, following custom, we describe thought and feeling as mental, I see no reason to exclude from that term any conscious state, and I would accept the definition of Russell,[2] who says: 'I hold that whatever we know without inference is mental.' It follows that mental experiences are the events in the universe of which we have the most direct knowledge. But, you may ask, if we accept the monistic view and say that the mind and the brain are two aspects of the same thing, is not this merely old-fashioned materialism brought up to date? But if the stuff of the universe that we know directly is mind, and matter is the same thing known only

[1] Loc. cit., 185.
[2] *Human Knowledge: Its Scope and Limits*, London, 1948, 240.

by means of conceptual symbols created by mind, it would seem as reasonable to call at least that part of reality mind as to call it matter. And matter, even crude matter, is not what it was. It has turned into energy, and the atom has become a pattern and the molecule a pattern of patterns, till all the different physical substances and their behaviour have come to be regarded as the outcome of the structure of their primitive components. But we have already met with pattern in the nervous system, underlying and rendering possible the most fundamental characteristics of the mind. And pattern in some mysterious way possesses a life of its own, for it can survive a change in the identity of its component parts as long as its structure remains the same. As a wave can move over the sea and remain the same wave, though the water of which it is composed is continuously changing, a pattern can shift over the retina and therefore over the visual area of the brain and remain recognizably the same pattern. The pattern of our personality though it changes slowly remains substantially the same, though every protein molecule in the body, including the nervous system, is changed three times a year.[1] The ingredients have altered but not the structure. How are we to envisage the physiological patterns upon which mental activity depends? Pitts and McCulloch[2] have employed complex mathematical formulae to explain the physiological basis of abstract thought and I do not think that anything simpler will serve. Consider what happens in the brain when we perceive a circle. As I have said earlier in this book, 'we might expect to find that there is something circular about the events in the cerebral cortex, for it is these, we are told, which are "projected" into the outside world when we perceive a circle. Nothing of the sort is

[1] E. C. Dodds, *Brit. Med. Journal*, 1950, **ii**, 1237.
[2] *Bull. Math. Phys.*, 1947, **9**, 127.

true. . . . When we perceive a two-dimensional circle we do so by means of an activity in the brain which is halved, reduplicated, transposed, inverted, distorted and three-dimensional.' One might add that as no two brains are exactly the same shape, the shape of the physiological disturbance is different in two people looking at the same circle. So the comparatively simple process of seeing a circle cannot be explained in terms of the spatial organization of the corresponding activity in the brain: it must, presumably, depend upon the development of complex relationships of these events in space and time, which we may find can be expressed only mathematically. Once again it is structure which is all-important. This world surely is very different from the world of the older materialists.

Our knowledge, as we have seen, is symbolic: our knowledge of the external world is based on perceptions which depend upon the physical structure of the sense-organs and nervous system. This in itself constitutes a limit to our perceptions; and it is likely enough that it sets bounds to our thought also. Need we believe that a nervous system evolved to facilitate action upon the physical world is capable of providing conceptual symbols adequate for the whole of reality? He is a bold man who would claim that to-day.

# VII

# THE STATUS OF MIND: A CONVERSATION BETWEEN READER AND AUTHOR

*Reader.* In following a detailed argument it's not always easy to see it as a whole. So will you give me a summary of your conclusions and then let me ask you some questions about them?

*Author.* I began with perception and tried to show that perceiving is not merely what at first sight it appears to be. I'm aware of a world of objects external to me and external to one another. The table over there is brown and hard; the orange on the table is scented and sweet; the bell sounds when struck; the sun in the sky is hot, and so on. But astronomers and physicists have inferred from their experiments with these and similar objects that light travels through space, and that I don't see the sun until nine minutes after the light wave which causes me to see it had left it; and, if in the meantime it had ceased to exist, I shouldn't be aware of the fact, but should still continue to see it for nine minutes after its extinction. The same applies to all other objects, including my own body. I can't see, hear, smell, taste, touch or feel them until after the lapse of time necessary for the appropriate physical disturbance to travel from the object to my body, and then the lapse of the further time required for the nerve-impulses aroused in the sense organ stimulated to travel through my ingoing nerves and central nervous system to the part of my brain concerned with sensation. And the neurophysiologist tells me that these nerve-impulses don't resemble the physical stimulus which arouses them, and, as far as is known, the only factor which determines what sensation we shall experience is the part of the brain which the nerve-impulse reaches. Moreover, if the parts of the brain concerned with sensation are excited in some other way—for example, by an electrical stimulus directly applied or by a discharge caused by a disease—the corresponding sensation is still experienced in consciousness. Hence, when we're aware of an object, the sensations by means of which we perceive it can't be part of the physical object, for their physical basis in the brain is the sole necessary condition of their occurrence, and this is physically unlike, and occurs later in time than, the physical events in the object which make me aware of it.

*Reader.* This is all very confusing. What happens when I see a table? I think I see a brown, flat object with four legs over there, but you tell me that is not the table. Is there one table or are there two? And if two, what is the relation between the one I see and the other one which I suppose you would call the physical table?

*Author.* The confusion is a verbal one: it all depends on what you mean by table. There is certainly a physical table which continues to exist when neither you nor anyone else is there to see it. If brownness is the conscious correlate of a certain state of the nervous system and of nothing else, the physical table cannot be said to be brown. When you say 'I see a table' you are normally using the same words to describe two things. The first is your experience of brownness, etc., which is the sensory element in seeing a table: the second is your awareness, through this experience, of a table as an object which continues to exist when you are not aware of it and which is other than the sensory elements by means of which you perceive it. Usually you don't need to distinguish these, for they occur simultaneously, and you call them both 'seeing a table'; but they're not the same thing. If you prefer to call them both tables there are two tables, but I think it is less confusing to speak either of the physical table and its perceptual representation, or of the perceptual table and its physical basis.

*Reader.* But if all that we know about objects is their perceptual representation, how do we ever get behind this? How do we know that the physical table exists at all? Are you not making the very mistake which Eddington made and which Susan Stebbing[1] exposed? You'll remember that she quoted a passage from his *New Pathways in Science* in which he maintained that colour, sound and scent cannot have been transmitted to us from the object in the external world to which we attribute them: they are spun by our own minds. Susan Stebbing then goes on: 'This is an amazing argument. The fact that we have knowledge of our nervous systems, the processes in the nerve fibres, and of states of the brain is used to establish the conclusion that we do not possess knowledge of the external world in which are to be found nervous systems, neural processes, and brain states. . . . To have such knowledge of the external world, I must surely have to compare the structure of what I perceive (i.e. the effect of the external stimulus) with the external source (i.e. the unknown cause of the perception). To compare an effect in my head with its wholly unknown cause does seem to be an impossible feat.'

*Author.* I'm glad you have mentioned Susan Stebbing because her brilliant, and in many respects just, criticism of Jeans and Eddington is well known, and her habitual lucidity is likely to appear convincing even when she is wrong. Indeed, it's probable that what confused Susan Stebbing will puzzle other people too. It must be admitted that Eddington contributes to the confusion in this instance. Let's see what really happens when we see a colour, and

[1] *Philosophy and the Physicists*, Penguin Books, London, 1944, 101.

how we learn about it. To begin with we—and by 'we' I mean not only ordinary people but all the scientists who have ever worked on the subject—start from the world of objects we perceive. We observe and experiment, and make inferences from what we see, and we conclude that light of a certain wave length is being reflected from the coloured object, passes through space, starts nerve-impulses, which are different in all respects from the wave length, in the retina, and that these travel by the optic nerves and reach the visual part of the brain. Thus our perceptions have enabled us to infer the physics and physiology of seeing, which prove that a chain of causation stretched from the object seen to the brain of the seer. But what happens at the surface of the object no more resembles what happens in the brain of the seer than the stone which runs down a mountain-side resembles the splash which it causes in the lake at the bottom. In seeing, awareness of the colour coincides with the brain state and corresponds to the splash in my analogy. Clearly it cannot be identical with what is happening at the object. We have arrived at this conclusion by using science to do just what Susan Stebbing said was essential; namely, by 'comparing the structure of what I perceive with the external source.' In what sense is this 'to establish the conclusion that we do not possess knowledge of the external world'?

There are three different but related questions here. (1) How can the nervous system, existing as one among all the other bodies in the physical world, yield information about bodies external to itself? (2) If our sensory experiences are purely subjective, how can they give us any information about the external world? (3) If our percepts are so different from the physical events which give rise to them, how can we infer the latter from the former? Since I am putting forward the view that consciousness and neural activity are

F

two aspects of the same thing, we can regard questions (1) and (2) as two ways of putting the same question. The nervous system is able to give information about the external world because one of its functions is symbolical representation. It provides symbols not only for external objects but also for relationships both between such objects and between them and the body. One relationship which the nervous system is thus able to symbolize is externality, and in making us aware of objects it makes us aware of them as external to ourselves. To express this in the terms of question (2), our sensory experiences of objects other than ourselves reach consciousness already stamped with externality. Whether the potentiality of this kind of knowledge is wholly innate or whether it is partly acquired or developed in infancy, we cannot remember a period in our lives when this was not the case. We do not need to infer that our experiences refer to the external world. I agree that if we did, it is difficult to see how we could ever reach such a conclusion. But this element in our experience is already given and intrinsic to it.

I think I've already partly answered the third question. Russell deals with it more fully in his Henry Sidgwick Lecture[1] in which he concludes: 'Percepts, considered causally, are between events in afferent nerves (stimulus) and events in efferent nerves (reaction); their location in causal chains is the same as that of certain events in the brain. Percepts as a source of knowledge of physical objects can only serve their purpose in so far as there are separable, more or less independent, causal chains in the physical world. This only happens approximately, and therefore the inference from percepts to physical objects cannot be precise. Science consists largely of devices for

[1] *Physics and Experience*, Cambridge, 1946. Reprinted in *Human Knowledge: Its Scope and Limits*, London, 1948, chap. 6.

overcoming this initial lack of precision on the assumption that perception gives a first approximation to the truth.' As Russell points out, 'one of the difficulties which have led to confusion was failure to distinguish between perceptual and physical space. Perceptual space consists of perceptible relations between parts of percepts, whereas physical space consists of inferred relations between inferred physical things. What I see may be outside my percept of my body, but not outside my body as a physical thing.'

*Reader.* But hasn't Russell himself lapsed into the same confusion in both the passages you've quoted? How can the location of percepts be the same as that of certain events in the brain, and how can what I see be inside my body as a physical thing?

*Author.* I agree that he has. Percepts are never anywhere but where they are perceived to be. It's their physical substratum, which we represent by the appropriate concepts of physics and physiology, which is in the physical brain— not the percept.

*Reader.* But, just a moment! Where is your physical brain? In your physical head. And you don't maintain, I suppose, that that isn't in the same place as your perceptual head! So within your head is the physical correlate of the colour which you perceive outside you, and you say that these are two aspects of the same thing. Can the same thing be in two places at the same time?

*Author.* Not in physical space, perhaps, though I shouldn't care to dogmatize about that; but you forget that you are dealing with perceptual space. There, awareness of a colour at a distance—the red of the setting sun, for example—is certainly simultaneous with a physiological process occurring in my head. But perceptual space is subject to its own laws and mustn't be confused with the space of physics, in which the external event which causes me to see the red of the setting sun occurs at an antecedent time to the event in my brain which constitutes my seeing it. The colour in perceptual space is not the cause of the brain-state which mediates it, nor is it the cause of my seeing, but in physical space the light waves which start, or are reflected, from the object are causally connected with both the brain-state and the associated awareness of the colour.

I agree with Ayer[1] when he says: 'The truth is not that the designations of "sense-data," "common-sense objects," and "scientific objects," refer to constituents of different "worlds," which lie in some mysterious way "beyond" one another . . . but simply that these designations belong to different languages, which are distinguished from one another, not by referring to different sorts of real objects, but by referring to phenomena in different ways.' I agree with him, further, that confusion arises if the physical is regarded as more 'real' than the perceptual, or conversely. Both are real.

*Reader.* Nevertheless, people often speak as though the physical 'world,' or the world which is represented by the concepts of physics, were in some way more 'real' than its perceptual representation. If perception and physics are merely two languages, why should one be closer to reality than the other?

*Author.* I think there are two reasons for this attitude. A language or other form of symbolical representation isn't identical with the things it stands for, and my perception of a table isn't identical with the table, and in certain respects it doesn't resemble the table at all. Since it's a language created by my nervous system and liable sometimes, as in dreams, to represent something which doesn't exist, it is felt to be coloured by its subjectivity. There's another reason. It's true that both perception and physics are

---

[1] *The Foundations of Empirical Knowledge*, London, 1946, 221.

symbolical representations of the world, but one system of symbolical representation may be more accurate, and therefore for certain purposes more useful, than another; and the conceptual system of physics is a more accurate representation of the world than perception affords, because it introduces corrections for the time-factors involved in perception, and thus enables us to infer the true spatial and temporal relations of bodies from their perceived relations. The concepts of physics are more accurate than perceptual representation also because they give us a great deal of information about the structure of the world—for example, atoms and electrons—which is far beyond the range of perception. This explains the tendency to speak of the physical representation of the world as 'more real' than the perceptual one. But it's not more actual: it's only more accurate, because it's more abstract; and, to achieve this, science has had to sacrifice the vividness and immediacy of representation which perception alone can give.

*Reader.* You maintain, then, that perception and scientific thought are two modes of symbolical representation of reality, and that both are mental activities. Does that tell us anything about the nature either of mind or of the reality which it thus represents?

*Author.* Not much, I'm afraid. It certainly doesn't mean that the reality of which we are aware is itself mental, nor does it exclude this possibility. As for mind itself, it merely tells us that one of its functions is symbolical representation. I've been almost exclusively concerned with this aspect of mind because it's of fundamental importance in relation to our knowledge of the world, but we mustn't lose sight of other and equally important mental functions. There are modes of thinking other than the scientific; and memory, emotion, will and self-consciousness could all receive as much attention as we have given to perception and scientific thought.

*Reader.* What have you to say about Ryle's views? Hasn't he finally demolished 'the ghost in the machine' and with it many of the functions you evidently attribute to the mind?

*Author.* It would take too long to discuss all the views which Ryle expresses in *The Concept of Mind*,[1] but I must comment on his ideas about sensation, observation and imagination, since if he's right about these I must be wrong, and, incidentally, his approach to these topics will illustrate what I believe to be the fundamental defect of his book.

*Reader.* Which is?

*Author.* The belief, comforting to a philosopher, that, to find out the nature of the mind, all one has to do is to sit in one's study and discuss the terms which are habitually used to describe activities defined as mental. For example, Ryle, in support of his thesis, is anxious to prove that sensations are not mental, that they do not exist in minds and that there is nothing private about them. Thus he says[2]: 'It is true that the cobbler cannot witness the tweaks that I feel when the shoe pinches. But it is false that I witness them. The reason why my tweaks cannot be witnessed by him is not that some iron curtain prevents them from being witnessed by anyone save myself, but that they are not the sorts of things of which it makes sense to say that they are witnessed or unwitnessed at all, even by me.' And again[3]: 'Sensations are neither observable nor unobservable. . . . Headaches cannot be witnessed, but they can be noticed, and while it is improper to advise a person not to peep at his tickle, it is quite proper to advise him not to pay any heed to it.' What Ryle has done here is to take words which he

---

[1] *The Concept of Mind*, London, 1949.      [2] Loc. cit., p. 205.
[3] Loc. cit., p. 206.

regards as connoting some mental activity—namely, wit-
nessing and observing—say that they are inapplicable to
sensations, and conclude that therefore sensations are not 'in
the mind'—which appears to me to be logically fallacious.
In any case, he has to admit that[1] 'I feel or have the tweaks,'
and the real question is not whether it makes sense to say
that tweaks are witnessed or unwitnessed or that sensations
are observable or unobservable, but why the cobbler cannot
feel or have the tweaks that I feel or have.

*Reader.* And how does Ryle answer that question?

*Author.* He says:[2] 'It is true and even tautologous that the
cobbler cannot feel the shoe pinching me, unless the cobbler
is myself, but this is not because he is excluded from a
peep-show open only to me, but because it would make no
sense to say that he was in my pain, and no sense, therefore,
to say that he was noticing the tweak that I was having.'
Ryle here seems to be expressing the same idea as Ayer[3]
when he says: 'The barriers that prevent us from enjoying
one another's experiences are not natural but logical.'
Ayer, however, goes on to point out that we ordinarily
employ two different sets of criteria for determining the
ownership of experiences; namely, continuity of disposition
and memory, and bodily continuity. He admits that it is
not inconceivable that A and B might both experience a
pain in B's body, and he concludes that if such experiences
were common we should alter our manner of speaking
to allow 'of there being only a single feeling of pain which
was experienced by both A and B.' But 'as we use words
at present, it must be held to be logically impossible that the
series of experiences that constitute the histories of different
people should ever intersect.' It is certainly not inconceivable, nor even perhaps impracticable, that two people
should experience the same pain. There seems no reason

[1] Loc. cit., p. 205.          [2] Loc. cit., p. 208.          [3] Loc. cit., p. 138.

why in a pair of Siamese twins a nerve should not be grafted from one into the other in such a way that a painful stimulus applied to A should cause B to feel a pain, and the experiment could either be arranged so that B felt the pain when A did not, or that they both felt it at the same time. In the latter event, though the experiences of A and B would be numerically different, it would seem no more illogical to say that they were experiencing the same pain than to say that they were seeing the same table when their visual experiences were identical in content. Thus, if it is true that 'it would make no sense' to say that the cobbler was feeling my pain, this is not because such an event is logically impossible, but only because it hasn't yet occurred. The reason why it has not is that the sensations of each of us are associated exclusively with changes in his own body, and the discontinuity of our bodies prevents another from sharing my pain and so excludes the cobbler from what Ryle disparagingly calls 'a peep-show open only to me.'

Ryle goes on to throw doubt upon the existence of sense-data. We observe objects, and[1] 'an object of observation, like a robin, or a cheese, must therefore be the sort of thing of which it is possible for observers to catch glimpses, or to get whiffs.' He then argues that if sensations are proper objects of observation the observer gets involved in an endless regress, because to observe a robin implies getting a glimpse of it, and, if that glimpse is a sensation, to observe that sensation means getting a glimpse of a glimpse, and so on indefinitely. But this also is surely a logical fallacy. Ryle admits that[2] 'observing entails having sensations,' but it doesn't follow that 'having sensations' is itself a form of observing, nor that it involves any process other than having them. A visual sensation may enable us to have a glimpse without itself being the appropriate object of a

[1] Loc. cit., p. 206.     [2] Loc. cit., p. 206.

glimpse. Ryle appears to regard sense-data as parts of objects, and he draws from this the conclusion that[1] 'we do not, consequently, have to rig up one theatre, called "the outside world," to house the common objects of anyone's observation, and another, called "the mind," to house the objects of some monopoly observations.' But naïve realism, as I have argued earlier, is refuted by the fact that glimpses and whiffs cannot be in 'the outside world,' where the objects they appear to belong to may long ago have ceased to exist.

Ryle's treatment of the imagination is again purely verbal. Images certainly seem private and subjective, and if he admits the existence of images he's in danger of conceding that they must exist 'in the mind': images, therefore, must be shown to be themselves imaginary. 'A person who[2] "sees Helvellyn in his mind's eye" is not seeing either the mountain or a likeness of the mountain; there is neither a mountain in front of the eyes in his face, nor a mock-mountain in front of any other non-facial eyes.' And[3] 'imaging occurs, but images are not seen. I do have tunes running in my head, but no tunes are being heard when I have them running there. True, a person picturing his nursery is, in a certain way, like that person seeing his nursery, but the similarity does not consist in his really looking at a real likeness of his nursery, but in his really seeming to see his nursery itself, when he is not really seeing it. He is not being a spectator of a resemblance of his nursery, but he is resembling a spectator of his nursery.' If you are a good visualizer you will know for yourself that Ryle is wrong in saying that imagining Helvellyn does not involve having a visual image of a mountain. But even his verbal evasion provides no escape from his difficulty, for, granted that a person picturing his nursery

[1] Loc. cit., p. 207.     [2] Loc. cit., p. 251.     [3] Loc. cit., p. 247.

resembles a spectator of his nursery, in what respect does he resemble him? Not in his relation to an object, for the nursery is no longer there and may have ceased to exist. The spectator of his nursery experiences visual sensations evoked by it: the man who imagines his nursery experiences visual images which resemble those sensations. Is not this how the one resembles the other? And, if not, what is the resemblance between them?

Ryle uses a similar verbal manoeuvre to try and escape from the implications of seeing double when what is seen is, in fact, single. He rejects the sense-datum view that the squinter[1] 'sees two bright somethings,' which are 'nothing but two proprietary "candle-looks," or sense-data,' for, he says,[2] 'the squinter, aware of his squint, who reports that it looks just as if there were two candles on the table, or that he might be seeing two candles, is describing how the single candle looks by referring to how pairs of candles regularly look to spectators who are not squinting; and if, not being aware of his squint, he says that there are two candles on the table, he is, in this case, misapplying just the same general recipe.' But, on Ryle's view of perception, when a person sees two candles, the things he sees are not private sense-data, but are two candles. This can't explain what the squinter sees, however, for in his case there is only one candle. What, then, is the status of the second 'candle' he sees? To describe his experience by saying that it is how two candles normally look is merely to state the problem but not to solve it. What in Ryle's view is the status of something which has a 'candle-look,' but which is not solid and whose flame will not burn his finger?

*Reader.* Do you believe, with the exponents of cybernetics, that the new mechanical principles embodied in electronic machines, such as calculating machines and

[1] Loc. cit., p. 216.        [2] Loc. cit., p. 217.

predictors which keep a gun aimed at a target, throw any light upon the working of the mind? Conversely, can we attribute mind or consciousness to such machines?

*Author.* Jefferson[1] has some wise things to say in answer to those questions. He points out that the physiological processes in the brain, however they resemble things in physical nature, and however amenable they are to examination as physio-chemical processes, persist in being unmistakably themselves. The brain, he says, however its functions may be mimicked by machines, remains itself and is unique in nature. I agree with all that he says, but I should like to try and express the same ideas in the terminology that I have been using in this book. Let's suppose, what is at present by no means proved, that the electrical experts have discovered and applied in their machines certain principles of functional organization which exist in the nervous system. What would follow from that? The view, which I have been putting forward, is that we can learn about the world in at least two ways, both of which are symbolical, or, if you prefer the term, representational. In perception the world is represented primarily by sensory symbols which are the product of the nervous system. By means of inferences from these we construct conceptual symbols which provide an alternative method of representing it. Neurophysiology uses conceptual symbols to describe the working of the nervous system and so to try to give an account of those processes which are known directly to us as thinking, willing, feeling, perceiving and so on—in fact, all the activities of mind. If we ask what light electro-physiological processes throw on the mind, or, conversely, whether mind as such can be attributed to non-living electrical organizations, we must realize that we are asking questions about the possible

[1] *Brit. Med. J.*, 1949, **i**, 1105.

correlations between two representational systems, or, in other words, we're inquiring how far two languages are mutually translatable. If we're to translate one language into another, it's essential that they shall both be at a similar stage of development, and that the same ideas shall be verbally represented in each. This condition isn't at present fulfilled when we come to consider the relationship between the nervous system and the mind. Our knowledge of neuro-anatomy and neurophysiology is still incomplete. We have much to learn about nerve-pathways and nervous function: and we know almost nothing about the neural basis of thought and feeling. Relatively simple concepts of nervous impulses and their integration are at present the only terms in the language of neurophysiology with which to interpret the whole gamut of mind. We are making a beginning, as I've shown in this book, in the task of correlating neuro-physiological function with mental activity, but so far our attempts in this sphere are little more than guesses, and it's possible, indeed, that conceptual scientific language applied to the nervous system will never prove adequate to the task of finding a full equivalence for mind. So, when the electrical experts claim to have detected in the physiology of the nervous system a likeness to their machines, they may or may not be right, but if they try to express that likeness in terms of the mind, they are guessing the meaning of a language of which they have not yet learned the alphabet. And if they seek on these grounds to endow machines with consciousness, they are assuming that because machines may resemble the nervous system in pattern they are, therefore, of the same nature.

\*    \*    \*    \*    \*

*Reader.* Is that all?

*Author.* It was going to be. Why?

*Reader.* Well, like most philosophers, you stop, tantalizingly, just when you seem to be getting to the most interesting point. When I read a book on philosophy I'm usually left asking: 'So, what?' If what you say is true, if your way of looking at things is right, what does it mean to the ordinary person; what practical difference does it make? Philosophers, nowadays at any rate, seem to pursue philosophy for its own sake and to take little interest in its implications and applications. In Yeats's words they 'cast a cold eye on life, on death.'

*Author.* Perhaps they do. At any rate, I'll try to tell you where I think these ideas lead. We live in an age dominated by abstract thought; we speak and think in the conceptual language of science. I believe that in a culture, as in an individual, there is on the whole an antagonism between abstract thought and those attitudes to life which are embodied in other kinds of symbolism. There is nothing new in this. Blake said: 'We impose on one another, and it is but lost time to converse with you whose works are only Analyticks.' But Blake's exasperation, however understandable, provided no means of overcoming the schism in the modern mind: it merely drove him into the unintelligible symbolism of 'The Four Zoas,' just as Yeats took refuge in his private 'Analyticks' of gyre and cone in 'A Vision.' The schism in a culture can be healed only in the minds of the individuals who belong to it, and the rejection of science is no solution. But as soon as we realize that science is only a language, and that many aspects of the 'invisible fabrick' of life can be better understood in other languages, and even in symbols other than words, we have opened the door to a great liberation of the spirit. Susanne Langer, in her profound work *Philosophy in a New Key*,[1] shows a way of escape from bondage to linguistic symbols.

[1] Cambridge, Massachusetts, 1951, 265.

'To us whose intelligence is bound up with language,' she writes, 'whose achievements are physical comforts, machines, medicines, great cities, and the means of their destruction, theory of knowledge means theory of communication, generalization, proof, in short: critique of science. But the limits of language are not the last limits of experience, and things inaccessible to language may have their own forms of conception, that is to say, their own symbolic devices.' And she examines from this point of view myth, sacrament, music, and the visual arts.

You quoted two of the three lines Yeats wrote for his own tombstone. But listen to the three together:

> 'Cast a cold eye
> On life, on death.
> Horseman, pass by!'

Do they not well express the conflict in the modern mind, and its reconciliation, which Yeats failed to achieve in himself? For man, while looking on the world with the 'cold eye' of scientific vision, still needs to be sustained and carried forward by the vital force of older modes of knowledge.

'Horseman, pass by!'

# INDEX

## ACKNOWLEDGEMENTS

I AM indebted to the following for their kind permission to publish copyright passages of prose or verse in this book: The Editors of *Brain and Philosophy;* Messrs. George Allen & Unwin, Limited, for extracts from *Human Knowledge in Scope and Limits*, by Bertrand Russell; The Cambridge University Press, for an extract from *Man on his Nature*, by Sir Charles Sherrington; Messrs. Faber & Faber, Limited, for extracts from *The Meaning of Art*, by Herbert Read; Messrs. Hutchinson & Company (Publishers) Limited, for extracts from *The Concept of Mind*, by Gilbert Ryle; Messrs. Macmillan & Company, Limited, for extracts from *The Foundations of Empirical Knowledge*, by A. J. Ayer; Messrs. Methuen & Company, Limited, for extracts from *Perception*, by H. H. Price; Miss Vivian Shepherd, for an extract from *Philosophy and the Physicists*, by the late Susan Stebbing; and Mrs. W. B. Yeats, Messrs. A. P. Watt & Son and Messrs. Macmillan & Company, Limited, for lines from one of the *Collected Poems* of W. B. Yeats.